Noble and Diana Franklin.

Read alone.

Finished June 1969

LIFE AND ADVENTURES OF ROBINSON CRUSOE

LIFE AND ADVENTURES OF ROBINSON CRUSOE

BY

DANIEL DEFOE

WARD LOCK & CO., LIMITED
LONDON AND MELBOURNE

517
MADE IN ENGLAND

Printed in Great Britain for Ward Lock & Co., Ltd.,
by C. Tinling & Co., Ltd., Liverpool, London and Prescot.

CONTENTS

BIOGRAPHICAL NOTICE

OF THE

AUTHOR OF "ROBINSON CRUSOE"

DANIEL DEFOE, the author of numerous works of fiction, among which the *History of the Plague* has obtained a certain popularity, and *Robinson Crusoe* a lasting and world-wide renown, was born in the parish of St. Giles, Cripplegate, in the city of London, in the year 1661. He was educated at a dissenting school at Newington Green; his father, a strict dissenter, intending him for the priesthood. But this project seems to have been abandoned, for some unknown reason, and young Daniel became a tradesman, like his father. Something of the roving, restless nature, so admirably described in *Robinson Crusoe*, seems to have been inherent in Defoe himself; for his life is full of strange vicissitudes, and he appears continually involved in trouble on one account or another. We find him taking part in the most ill-considered and unfortunate enterprise of his time, the Rebellion of Monmouth, and narrowly escaping what the cynical spirit of the time dubbed "a merry go-round at rope fair," namely, death by strangulation, for the offence. In after-life he was hotly embroiled in the political quarrels of his age. At one time he was compelled to stand in the pillory, as a punishment for writing a well-timed and thoughtful pamphlet on *The Shortest Way with the Dissenters*. The populace, sympathising with and admiring him, crowned the pillory with flowers, and converted his penance into a triumph; but this could not relieve him from the burden of the heavy fine he was compelled to pay, and which hampered him for years afterwards. At another time he suffered a long imprisonment, obtaining his release after two years by the intervention of Harley, Earl of Oxford. But he had not the art of advancing his fortunes, though his evident merit procured him employment in several matters of consequence; and, at the end of his long life, he was in poverty and neglect. He died in his native parish of St. Giles, Cripplegate, April 24, 1731, at the age of seventy, and was interred in Bunhill Fields burial ground.

The political works of Defoe are numerous, and had a sensible effect on the times in which he lived. A thorough Englishman, out-spoken, vehement, and uncompromising, he shouted out lustily against abuses and wrong-doing wherever he found them; and in many respects his ideas were greatly in advance of his time. Some of his schemes may have been visionary and impracticable; but it is pleasant to hear his sturdy voice raised, and see his nervous pen wielded so unflinchingly in advocacy of his principles, and to mark how unvaryingly those principles point to moderation, mercy, and the law of kindness. His Review, which he conducted for nine years, may certainly be considered as the pioneer of the *Spectator*, *Tatler*, *Guardian*, and other collections of essays which enriched the literature of the first half of the eighteenth century.

His political writings, however, have mostly passed away with the troublous times which gave them birth, and to which their interest was confined. It was as a writer of fiction that Defoe was to achieve more lasting fame. Two at least of his works have a value and a significance quite irrespective of time and place—the one as a record of a national calamity, the other as a wonderful piece of imaginary autobiography. These two books are the *History of the Plague of* 1665, and the *Adventures of Robinson Crusoe.*

At the time when the scourge was decimating London, Daniel Defoe was only four years old. It could not, therefore, be from memory that he so vividly described its incidents; though, doubtless, in his youth he heard many an anecdote about the pestilence and its ravages, from men of maturer years, on whose memories it must have made an indelible impression. But his chief talent lay in the management of detail and accurate description; and it is difficult to imagine as we read the graphic record of the state of the terror-stricken, desolate city, that we have not before us the real daily notes of an actual indweller in the city of the plague. In *Robinson Crusoe* the same marvellous power is shown, but in a much higher degree.

With matchless skill, the doubts and sorrows, the shifts and expedients, the little domestic triumphs and disappointments of the shipwrecked mariner in his solitary home are put before the reader in the very form most calculated to enlist his interests and sympathies. So thoroughly has the author identified himself with the hero of his romance, that Defoe disappears, and it is Robinson Crusoe himself who becomes a living personality, and moves and speaks before the reader, and becomes as clearly and distinctly personified as any hero of real life.

The first edition of *Robinson Crusoe* was published in 1719. During the period that has since elapsed, hundreds of editions have appeared in all European languages. Everywhere the book has worked its way; and as for the German version, *Robinson de Jungere* is chronicled as one of the greatest successes of the eminent Hamburg firm of Campe and Co.

In the present volume, the original text, slightly shortened, has been adhered to. The operation of modernising the language, necessary, perhaps, in a scientific work, would have taken away one of the chief charms from the narrative of the simple sailor, who is therefore left to tell his tale in his own rough, pathetic, old-fashioned way.

SECTION I

ROBINSON'S FAMILY, ETC.—HIS ELOPEMENT FROM HIS PARENTS

I WAS born in the year 1632, in the city of York, of a good family, though not of that country, my father being a foreigner of Bremen, named Kreutznaer, who settled first at Hull. He got a good estate by merchandise, and leaving off his trade, lived afterwards at York; from whence he had married my mother, whose relations were named Robinson, a very good family in that country, and after whom I was so called, that is to say, Robinson Kreutznaer; but, by the usual corruption of words in England, we are now called, nay, we call ourselves, and write our name, Crusoe; and so my companions always called me.

I had two elder brothers, one of whom was lieutenant-colonel to an English regiment of foot in Flanders, formerly commanded by the famous Colonel Lockhart, and was killed at the battle near Dunkirk against the Spaniards. What became of my second brother, I never knew, any more than my father and mother did know what was become of me.

Being the third son of the family, and not bred to any trade, my head began to be filled very early with rambling thoughts. My father, who was very aged, had given me a competent share of learning, as far as house education and a country free school generally go, and designed me for the law; but I would be satisfied with nothing but going to sea; and my inclination to this led me so strongly against the will, nay, the commands of my father, and against all the entreaties and persuasions of my mother and other friends, that there seemed to be something fatal in that propension of nature, tending directly to the life of misery which was to befall me.

My father, a wise and grave man, gave me serious and excellent counsel against what he foresaw was my design. He called me one morning into his chamber, where he was confined by the gout, and expostulated very warmly with me upon this subject; he asked me what reasons, more than a mere wandering inclination, I had for leaving his house, and my native country, where I might be well introduced, and had a prospect of raising my fortune, by application and industry, with a life of ease and pleasure. He told me it was men of desperate fortunes, on one hand, or of superior fortunes, on the other, who went abroad upon adventures, aspiring to rise by enterprise, and make themselves famous in undertakings of nature out of the common road; that these things were all either too far above me, or too far below me; that mine was the middle state, or what might be called the upper station of low life, which he had found, by long experience, was the best state in the world, the most suited to human happiness; not exposed to the miseries and hardships, the labour and sufferings, of the mechanic part of mankind, and not embarrassed with the pride, luxury, ambition, and envy of the upper part of mankind: he told me, I might judge of the happiness of this state by one thing, viz., that this was the state of life which all other people envied; that kings have frequently lamented the miserable consequences of being born to great things, and wished they had been placed in the middle of two extremes, between the mean and the great; that the wise man gave his testimony to this as the just standard of true felicity, when he prayed to have "neither poverty nor riches."

He bade me observe it, and I should always find, that the calamities of life were shared among the upper and lower part of mankind; but that the middle station had the fewest disasters, and was not exposed to so many vicissitudes as the higher or lower part of mankind; nay, they were not subjected to so many distempers and uneasinesses, either of body or mind, as those were, who, by vicious living, luxury, and extravagances, on one hand, or, by hard labour, want of necessaries, and mean and insufficient diet, on the other hand, bring distempers upon themselves by the natural consequences of their way of living; that the middle station of life was calculated for all kind of virtues, and all kind of enjoyments; that peace and plenty were the handmaids of a middle fortune; that temperance, moderation, quietness, health, society, all agreeable diversions, and all desirable pleasures were the blessings attending the middle station of life; that this way men went silently and smoothly through the world, and comfortably out of it, not embarrassed with the labours of the hands or of the head, not sold to the life of slavery for daily bread, or harassed with perplexed circumstances, which rob the soul of peace, and the body of rest; not enraged with the passion of envy, or secret burning lust of ambition for great things; but, in easy circumstances, sliding gently through the world, and sensibly tasting the sweets of living, without the bitter; feeling that they are happy, and learning by every day's experience, to know it more sensibly.

After this he pressed me earnestly, and in the most affectionate manner, not to play the young man, nor to precipitate myself into miseries which nature, and the station of life I was born in, seemed to have provided against.

I observed the tears run down his face very plentifully, especially when he spoke of my brother who was killed; and that, when he spoke of my having leisure to repent, and none to assist me, he was so moved, that he broke off the discourse, and told me his heart was so full, he could say no more to me.

I was sincerely affected with this discourse; as, indeed, who could be otherwise? and I resolved not to think of going abroad any more, but to settle at home, according to my father's desire. But alas! a few days wore it all off: and, in short, to prevent any of my father's further importunities, in a few weeks after I resolved to run quite away from him. However, I did not act so hastily, neither, as my first heat of resolution prompted; but I took my mother, at a time when I thought her a little pleasanter than ordinary, and told her that my thoughts were so entirely bent upon seeing the world, that I should never settle to anything with resolution enough to go through with it, and my father had better give me his consent than force me to go without it; that I was now eighteen years old, which was too late to go apprentice to a trade, or clerk to an attorney; that I was sure, if I did, I should never serve out my time, and I should certainly run away from my master before my time was out, and go to sea; and if she would speak to my father to let me make but one voyage abroad, if I came home again, and did not like it

I would go no more; and I would promise by a double diligence, to recover the time I had lost.

This put my mother in a great passion: she told me she knew it would be to no purpose to speak to my father upon any such a subject; that he knew too well what was my interest to give his consent to anything so much for my hurt; and that she wondered how I could think of any such thing, after such a discourse as I had from my father, and such kind and tender expressions as she knew my father had used: that for her part, she would not have so much hand in my destruction; and I should never have it to say, that my mother was willing when my father was not.

Though my mother refused to move it to my father, yet, as I have heard afterwards, she reported all the discourse to him; and that my father, after showing a great concern at it, said to her with a sigh: "That boy might be happy if he would stay at home; but if he goes abroad, he will be the most miserable wretch that ever was born; I cannot give consent to it."

It was not till almost a year after this that I broke loose; though in the meantime I continued obstinately deaf to all proposals of settling to business, and frequently expostulating with my father and mother about their being so positively determined against what they knew my inclinations prompted me to. But being one day at Hull, whither I went casually, and without any purpose of making an elopement at that time, and one of my companions then going to London by sea in his father's ship, and prompting me to go with them by the common allurement of seafaring men, viz., that it should cost me nothing for my passage, I consulted neither father nor mother any more, nor so much as sent them word of it; but left them to hear of it as they might, without asking God's blessing, or my father's, without any consideration of circumstances or consequences, and in an ill hour, God knows.

SECTION II

FIRST ADVENTURES AT SEA, AND EXPERIENCE OF A MARITIME LIFE—VOYAGE TO GUINEA

On the 1st September, 1651, I went on board a ship bound for London. Never any young adventurer's misfortunes, I believe, began sooner, or continued longer, than mine. The ship had no sooner got out of the Humber, than the wind began to blow, and the waves to rise, in a most frightful manner; and as I had never been at sea before, I was most inexpressibly sick in body, and terrified in mind; I began now seriously to reflect upon what I had done, and how justly I was overtaken by the judgment of Heaven, for wickedly leaving my father's house. All the good counsels of my parents, my father's tears, and my mother's entreaties, came now fresh to my mind; and my conscience, which was not yet come to the pitch of hardness to which it has been since, reproached me with the contempt of advice, and the abandonment of my duty.

All this while the storm increased, and the sea, which I had never been upon before, went very high though nothing like what I have seen many times since; no, not what I saw a few days after; but, such as it was, enough to affect me then, who was but a young sailor, and had never known anything of the matter. I expected every wave would have swallowed us up, and that every time the ship fell down, as I thought, in the trough or hollow of the sea, we should never rise more; and in this agony of mind I made many vows and resolutions that if it would please God to spare my life this voyage, if ever I got my foot once on dry land, I would go directly home to my father, and never set it into a ship again while I lived; that I would take his advice, and never run myself into such miseries as these any more. Now I saw plainly the goodness of his observations about the middle station of life; how easy, how comfortable, he had lived all his days, and never had been exposed to tempests at sea or troubles on shore; and I resolved that I would, like a true repenting prodigal, go home to my father.

These wise and sober thoughts continued during the storm, and indeed some time after; but the next day, as the wind was abated, and the sea calmer, I began to be a little inured to it. However, I was very grave that day, being also a little sea-sick still; but towards night the weather cleared up, the wind was quite over, and a charming fine evening followed: the sun went down perfectly clear, and rose so the next morning; and having little or no wind, and a smooth sea, the sun shining upon it, the sight was, as I thought, the most delightful that I ever saw.

I had slept well in the night, and was now no more sea-sick, but very cheerful, looking with wonder upon the sea that was so rough and terrible the day before, and could be so calm and pleasant in a little time after.

In a word, as the sea was returned to its smoothness of surface and settled calmness by the abatement of the storm, so the hurry of my thoughts being over, my fears and apprehensions of being swallowed up by the sea forgotten, and the current of my former desires returned, I entirely forgot the vows and promises I had made in my distress.

The sixth day of our being at sea we came into Yarmouth Roads; the wind having been contrary and the weather calm, we had made but little way since the storm. Here we were obliged to come to an anchor, and here we lay, the wind continuing contrary, viz., at south-west, for seven or eight days, during which time a great many ships from Newcastle came into the same roads, as a common harbour where the ships might wait for a wind for the river Thames. We had not, however, rid here so long, but we should have tided up the river, but that the wind blew too fresh; and, after we had lain four or five days, blew very hard. However, the roads being reckoned as good as a harbour, the anchorage good, and our ground tackle very strong, our men were unconcerned, and not in the least apprehensive of danger, but spent the time in rest and mirth, after the manner of the sea. But the eighth day, in the morning, the wind increased, and we had all hands at work to strike our topmasts, and make everything snug and close, that the ship might ride as easy as possible. By noon the sea went very high indeed, and our ship rode forecastle in, shipped several seas, and we thought once or twice our anchor had come home; upon which our master ordered out the sheet anchor; so that we rode with two anchors ahead, and cables veered out to the better end.

In the middle of the night, and under all the rest of our distresses, one of the men, that had been down on purpose to see, cried out, " We have sprung a leak ! " another man said " there was four foot of water in the hold." Then all hands were called to the pump. At that very word, my heart, as I thought, died within me, and I fell backwards upon the side of my bed, where I sat in the cabin. However, the men roused me, and told me that I, who was able to do nothing before, was as well able to pump as another; at which I stirred up and went to the pump, and worked very heartily. While this was doing, the master seeing some light colliers, who, not able to ride out the storm, were obliged to slip and run away to sea, and would not come near us, ordered us to fire a gun as a signal of distress. I, who knew nothing what that meant, was so surprised, that I thought the ship had broke, or some dreadful thing had happened. In a word, I was so surprised, that I fell down in a swoon. As this was a time when everybody had his own life to think of, no one minded me, or what was become of me; but another man stepped up to the pump, and thrusting me aside with his foot, let me lie, thinking I had been dead; and it was a great while before I came to myself.

We worked on; but the water increasing in the hold, it was apparent that the ship would founder; and though the storm began to abate a little, yet as it was not possible she could swim till we might run into a port;—so, the master continued firing guns for help; and a light ship, who had rid it out just ahead of us, ventured a boat out to help us. It was with the utmost hazard the boat came near us, but it was impossible for us to get on board, or for the boat to lie near the ship's side; till at last the men rowing very heartily, and venturing their lives to save ours, our men cast them a rope over our stern with a buoy to it, and then veered it out a great length, which they, after great labour and hazard, took hold of, and we hauled them close under our stern, and all got into the boat. It was to no purpose for them or us, after we were in the boat, to think of reaching their own ship; so all agreed to let her drive, and only to pull her in towards shore as much as we could; and our master promised them, that if the boat were staved upon the shore, he would make it good to their master; so partly rowing and partly driving, our boat went away to the northward, sloping towards the shore almost as far as Winterton-Ness.

We were not much more than a quarter of an hour out of our ship when we saw her sink; and then I understood, for the first time, what was meant by a ship foundering in the sea. I must acknowledge, I had hardly eyes to look up when the seamen told me she was sinking; for, from that moment, they rather put me into the boat than that I might be said to go in. My heart was, as it were, dead within me, partly with fright, partly with horror of mind, and the thoughts of what was yet before me.

While we were in this condition, the men yet labouring at the oar, to bring the boat near the shore, we could see (when, our boat mounting the waves, we were able to see the shore) a great many people running along the strand, to assist us when we should come near; but we made but slow way towards the shore; nor were we able to reach it, till being past the lighthouse at Winterton, the shore falls off to the westward, towards Cromer, and so the land broke off a little the violence of the wind. Here we got in, and, though not without much difficulty, got all safe on shore, and walked afterwards on foot to Yarmouth; where, as unfortunate men, we were used with great humanity, as well by the magistrates of the town, who assigned us good quarters, as by the particular merchants and owners of ships; and had money given us sufficient to carry us either to London or back to Hull, as we thought fit.

Had I now had the sense to have gone back to Hull, and have gone home, I had been happy: and my father, an emblem of our blessed Saviour's parable, had even killed the fatted calf for me; for, hearing the ship I went in was cast away in Yarmouth Roads, it was a great while before he had any assurance that I was not drowned.

As for me, having some money in my pocket, I travelled to London by land; and there, as well as on the road, had many struggles with myself what course of life I should take, and whether I should go home or go to sea. As to going home, shame opposed the best motions that offered to my thoughts and it immediately occurred to me how I should be laughed at among the neighbours, and should be ashamed to see, not my father and mother only, but even everybody else. From whence I have often observed, how incongruous and irrational the common temper of mankind is, especially of youth, to that reason which ought to guide them in such cases, viz., that they are not ashamed to sin, and yet are ashamed to repent; not ashamed of the action for which they ought justly to be esteemed fools; but are ashamed of the returning, which only can make them be esteemed wise men.

I went on board a vessel bound to the coast of Africa; or as the sailors vulgarly call it, a voyage to Guinea.

It was my lot, first of all, to fall into pretty good company in London; I became acquainted with the master of a ship, who had been on the coast of Guinea, and who, having had very good success there, was resolved to go again. He, hearing me say I had a mind to see the world, told me, that if I would go that voyage with him, I should be at no expense; I should be his messmate and his companion; and if I could carry anything with me, I should have all the advantage of it the trade would admit, and perhaps I might meet with some encouragement. I embraced the offer, and, entering into strict friendship with this captain, who was an honest and plain-dealing man, I went the voyage with him, and carried a small adventure with me; which, by the disinterested honesty of my friend the captain, I increased very considerably; for I carried about forty pounds in such toys and trifles as the captain directed me to buy. This forty pounds I mustered together by the assistance of some of my relations whom I corresponded with; and who, I believe, got my father, or at least, my mother, to contribute so much as that to my first adventure. This was the only voyage which I may say was successful in all my adventures, and which I owe to the integrity and honesty of my friend the captain; under whom also I got a competent knowledge of mathematics and the rules of navigation, learned how to keep an account of the ship's course, take an observation, and, in short, to understand some things that were needful to be understood by a sailor; for, as he took delight to instruct me, I took delight to learn; and, in a word, this voyage made me both a sailor and a merchant; for I brought home five pounds nine ounces of gold dust for my adventures, which yielded me in London, on my return, almost three hundred pounds, and this filled me with those aspiring thoughts which have since so completed my ruin. Yet even in this voyage, I had my misfortunes, too; particularly, that I was continually sick, being thrown into a violent calenture by the excessive heat of the climate; our principal trading being upon the coast from the latitude of fifteen degrees north, even to the line itself.

SECTION III

ROBINSON'S CAPTIVITY AT SALLEE—ESCAPE WITH XURY—ARRIVAL AT THE BRAZILS

I WAS now set up for a Guinea trader; and my friend, to my great misfortune, dying soon after his arrival, I resolved to go the same voyage again; and I embarked in the same vessel with one who was his mate in the former voyage, and had now got the command of the ship. This was the unhappiest voyage that ever man made; for though I did not carry quite a hundred pounds of my new-gained wealth, so that I had two hundred pounds left, and which I lodged with my friend's widow, who was very just to me, yet I fell into terrible misfortunes in this voyage; and the first was this, viz.—our ship, making her course towards the Canary Islands, or rather between those Islands and the African shore, was surprised in the grey of the morning, by a Turkish rover, of Sallee, who gave chase to us, with all the sail she could make. We crowded also as much canvas as our yards would spread, or our masts carry, to get clear; but finding the pirate gained upon us, and would certainly come up with us in a few hours, we prepared to fight, our ship having twelve guns and the rover eighteen. About three in the afternoon he came up with us; and bringing to by mistake, just athwart our quarter, instead of athwart our stern, as he intended, we brought eight of our guns to bear on that side, and poured in a broadside upon him, which made him sheer off again, after returning our fire, and pouring in also his small shot from near two hundred men whom he had on board. However, we had not a man touched, all our men keeping close. He prepared to attack us again, and we to defend ourselves; but laying us on board the next time upon our other quarter, he entered sixty men upon our decks, who immediately fell to cutting and hacking the sails and rigging. We plied them with small shot, half-pikes, powder-chests, and such like, and cleared our decks of them twice. However, to cut short this melancholy part of our story, our ship being disabled, and three of our men killed, and eight wounded, we were then obliged to yield, and were all carried prisoners into Sallee, a port belonging to the Moors.

The usage I had there was not so dreadful as at first I apprehended; nor was I carried up the country to the emperor's court, as the rest of our men were, but was kept by the captain of the rover as his proper prize and made his slave, being young and nimble, and fit for his business.

As my new patron, or master, had taken me home to his house, so I was in hopes he would take me with him when he went to sea again, believing that it would, some time or other, be his fate to be taken by a Spanish or Portuguese man of war, and that then I should be set at liberty. But this hope of mine was soon taken away, for when he went to sea he left me on shore to look after his little garden and do the common drudgery of slaves about his house; and when he came home again from his cruise, he ordered me to lie in the cabin, to look after the ship.

Here I meditated nothing but my escape, and what method I might take to effect it, but found no way that had the least probability in it. Nothing presented to make the supposition of it rational; for I had nobody to communicate it to that would embark with me; no fellow-slave, no Englishman, Irishman, or Scotchman there but myself; so that for two years, though I often pleased myself with the imagination, yet I never had the least encouraging prospect of putting it in practice.

After about two years, an odd circumstance presented itself, which put the old thought of making some attempt for my liberty again into my head. My patron lying at home longer than usual without fitting out his ship, which, as I heard, was for want of money, he used constantly, once or twice a week, sometimes oftener if the weather was fair, to take the ship's pinnace, and go out into the roads a fishing; and as he always took me and a young Moresco with him to row the boat, we made him very merry, and I proved very dexterous in catching fish, insomuch that sometimes he would send me with a Moor, one of his kinsmen, and the youth the Moresco, as they called him, to catch a dish of fish for him.

It happened one time, that going a fishing in a stark calm morning, a fog rose so thick, that though we were not half a league from the shore, we lost sight of it; and rowing, we knew not whither, or which way, we laboured all day, and all the next night, and when the morning came, we found we had pulled off to sea, instead of pulling in for the shore, and that we were at least two leagues from the shore; however, we got well in again, though with a great deal of labour, and some danger, for the wind began to blow pretty fresh in the morning; but particularly we were all very hungry.

But our patron, warned by this disaster, resolved to take more care of himself for the future; and having lying by him the long-boat of our English ship he had taken, he resolved he would not go a fishing any more without a compass and some provision; so he ordered the carpenter of the ship, who was an English slave, to build a little state-room or cabin in the middle of the longboat, like that of a barge, with a place to stand behind it, to steer and haul home the main sheet, and room before for a hand or two to stand and work the sails. She sailed with what we called a leg-of-mutton sail, and the boom jibbed over the top of the cabin, which lay very snug and low, and had in it room for him to lie, with a slave or two, and a table to eat on, with some small lockers to put in some bottles of such liquor as he thought fit to drink, and particularly his bread, rice, and coffee.

We went frequently out with this boat a fishing, and as I was most dexterous to catch fish for him, he never went without me. It happened that he had appointed to go out in this boat, either for pleasure or for fish, with two or three Moors of some distinction in that place, and for whom he had provided extraordinarily, and had therefore sent on board the boat, overnight, a larger stock of provisions than ordinary and had ordered me to get ready three fuses, with powder and shot, which were on board his ship, for that they designed some sport of fowling as well as fishing.

I got all things ready as he directed, and waited the next morning with the boat washed clean, her ensign and pendants out, and everything to accommodate his guests: when, by and by, my patron came on board alone, and told me his guests had put off going, upon some business that fell out, and ordered me, with a man and a boy, as usual, to go out with the boat, and catch them some fish, for that his friends were to sup at his house; and commanded, that as soon as I had got some fish, I should bring it home to his house; all which I prepared to do.

This moment my former notions of deliverance darted into my thoughts, for now I found I was like to have a little ship at my command; and my master being gone, I prepared to furnish myself, not for a fishing business, but for a voyage; though I knew not, neither did I so much as consider, whither I should steer; for any where, to get out of that place, was my way.

My first contrivance was to make a pretence to speak to this Moor, to get something for our subsistence on board; for I told him we must not presume to eat of our patron's bread; he said, that was true; so he brought a large basket of rusk or biscuit, of their kind, and three jars of fresh water, into the boat. I knew where my patron's case of bottles stood, which it was evident, by the make, were taken out of some English prize, and I conveyed them into the boat while the Moor was on shore, as if they had been there before for our master. I conveyed also a great lump of bees-wax into the boat, which weighed above half-a-hundredweight, with a parcel of twine or thread, a hatchet, a saw, and a hammer, all which were of great use to us afterwards, especially the wax, to make candles. Another trick I tried upon him, which he innocently came into also; his name was Ishmael, whom they called Muley, or Moley; so I called to him: "Moley," said I, "our patron's guns are on board the boat, can you not get a little powder and shot? It may be that we may kill some alcamies (fowls like our curlews) for ourselves, and I know he keeps the gunner's stores in the ship." "Yes," says he, "I will bring some"; and accordingly he brought a great leathern pouch, which held about a pound and a half of powder, or rather more, and another with shot, that had five or six pounds, with some bullets, and put all into the boat; at the same time I found some powder of my master's in the great cabin, with which I filled one of the large bottles in the case, which was almost empty, pouring what was in it into another; and thus furnished with everything needful, we sailed out of port to fish. The castle, which is at the entrance of the port, knew who we were, and took no notice of us; and we were not above a mile out of the port, when we hauled in our sail, and set us down to fish. The wind blew from N.N.E., which was contrary to my desire; for, had it blown southerly, I had been sure to have made the coast of Spain, and at last reached to the bay of Cadiz; but my resolutions were, blow which way it would, I would be gone from the horrid place where I was, and leave the rest to fate.

After we had fished some time and caught nothing, for when I had a fish on my hook I would not pull it up, that he might not see it, I said to the Moor: "This will not do; our master will not be served thus; we must stand further off." He, thinking no harm, agreed; and being at the head of the boat, set the sails; and as I had the helm, I run the boat near a league farther, and then brought to, as if I would fish. Then giving the boy the helm, I stepped forward to where the Moor was, and I took him by surprise, with my arm under his waist, and tossed him clean overboard into the sea. He rose immediately, for he swam like a cork, and called to me, begged to be taken in, and told me he would go all the world over with me. He swam so strong after the boat, that he would have reached me very quickly, there being but little wind; upon which I stepped into the cabin, and fetching one of the fowling-pieces, I presented it at him, and told him, I had done him no hurt, and if he would be quiet, I would do him none. "But," said I, "you swim well enough to reach the shore, and the sea is calm; make the best of your way to shore, and I will do you no harm; but if you come near the boat, I will shoot you through the head; for I am resolved to have my liberty." So he turned himself about, and swam for the shore; and I make no doubt but he reached it with ease, for he was an excellent swimmer.

I could have been content to have taken this Moor with me and have drowned the boy, but there was no venturing to trust him. When he was gone, I turned to the boy, whom they called Xury, and said to him, "Xury, if you will be faithful to me I will make you a great man; but if you will not stroke your face to be true to me (that is, swear by Mahomet and his father's beard), I must throw you into the sea too." The boy smiled in my face, and spoke so innocently, that I could not mistrust him; and swore to be faithful to me, and go all over the world with me.

While I was in view of the Moor that was swimming, I stood out directly to sea with the boat, rather stretching to windward, that they might think me gone towards the Straits' mouth (as indeed anyone that had been in their wits must have been supposed to do); for who would have supposed we were sailing on to the southward, to the truly Barbarian coast, where whole nations of negroes were sure to surround us with their canoes, and destroy us; where we could never once go on shore but we should be devoured by savage beasts, or more merciless savages of human kind?

But as soon as it grew dusk in the evening I changed my course, and steered directly south and by east, bending my course a little towards the east, that I might keep in with the shore; and having a fair fresh gale of wind, and a smooth quiet sea, I made such sail, that I believe by the next day, at three o'clock in the afternoon, when I made the land, I could not be less than one hundred and fifty miles south of Sallee, quite beyond the Emperor of Morocco's dominions, or indeed of any other king thereabout; for we saw no people.

Yet such was the fright I had taken at the Moors, and the dreadful apprehensions I had of falling into their hands, that I would not stop, or go on shore, or come to an anchor, the wind continuing fair, till I had sailed in that manner five days; and then the wind shifting to the southward, I concluded also that if any of our vessels were in chase of me, they also would now give over; so I ventured to make to the coast, and came to an anchor in the mouth of a little river; I knew, not what or where, neither what latitude, what country, what nation, or what river. I neither saw, nor desired to see, any people; the principal thing I wanted was fresh water. We came into this creek in the evening, resolving to swim on shore as soon as it was dark, and discover the country; but as soon as it was quite dark, we heard such dreadful noises of the barking, roaring, and howling of wild creatures, of we knew not what kinds, that the poor boy was ready to die with fear, and begged of me not to go on shore till day. "Well, Xury," said I, "then I will not; but it may be we shall see men by day, who will be as bad to us as those lions." "Then we may give them the shoot-gun," says Xury, laughing "make them run away." Such English Xury spoke by conversing among us slaves. However, I was glad to see the boy so cheerful, and I gave him a dram out of our patron's case of bottles to cheer him up. After all, Xury's advice was good, and I took it. We dropped our little anchor, and lay still all night; I say still, for we slept none; for in two or three hours we saw vast creatures (we knew not what to call them), of many sorts, come down to the sea-shore, and run into the water, wallowing and washing themselves, for the pleasure of cooling themselves; and they made such howlings and yellings, that I never indeed heard the like.

Xury was dreadfully frightened, and indeed so was I too; but we were both more frightened when we heard one of these creatures swimming towards our boat; and we could hear by his blowing that he was a monstrous, huge and furious beast. Poor Xury cried to me to weigh the anchor and row away. "No," says I, "Xury, we can slip our cable with a buoy to it, and go off to sea; they cannot follow us far." I had no sooner said so, when I perceived the creature within two oars' length, which surprised me; however, I immediately stepped to the cabin door, and taking up my gun, fired at him; upon which he immediately turned about, and swam to the shore again.

It is impossible to describe the horrible noises, and hideous cries and howlings that were raised, as well upon the edge of the shore as higher within the country, upon the noise or report of the gun; a thing, I believe, those creatures had never heard before. This convinced me there was no going on shore for us in the night upon that coast; and how to venture on shore in the day, was another question too; for to have fallen into the hands of any of the savages, had been as bad as to have fallen into the paws of lions and tigers; at least, we were equally apprehensive of the danger of it.

Be that as it would, we were obliged to go on shore somewhere or other for water, for we had not a pint left in the boat; when and where to get it was the point. Xury said if I would let him go on shore with one of the jars, he would find if there was any water, and bring some to me. I asked him why he would go; why I should not go, and he stay in the boat. The boy answered with so much affection, that he made me love him ever after. Says he, "If wild mans come, they eat me, you go away." "Well, Xury," said I, "we will both go; and if the wild mans come, we will kill them; they shall eat neither of us." So I gave Xury a piece of rusk bread to eat, and a dram out of our patron's case of bottles, which I mentioned before; and we hauled in the boat as near the shore as we thought was proper, and so waded to shore, carrying nothing but our arms, and two jars for water.

I did not care to go out of sight of the boat, fearing the coming of canoes with savages down the river; but the boy, seeing a low place about a mile up the country, rambled to it; and, by and by, I saw him come running towards me. I thought he was pursued by some savage or frightened by some wild beast, and I therefore ran forward to help him; but when I came nearer to him, I saw something hanging over his shoulders, which was a creature that he had shot, like a hare, but different in colour, and with longer legs; however, we were very glad of it, and it was very good meat; but the great joy that poor Xury came with, was to tell me he had found good water, and seen no wild mans.

As I had been one voyage to this coast before, I knew very well that the islands of the Canaries, and the Cape de Cerd Islands also, lay not far from the coast. But as I had no instruments to take an observation, to find what latitude we were in, and did not exactly know, or at least remember, what latitude they were in, I knew not where to look for them, or when to stand off to sea towards them, otherwise I might now have easily found some of these islands. But my hope was that if I stood along this coast till I came to the part where the English traded, I should find some of their vessels upon their usual design of trade, that would relieve and take us in.

By the best of my calculation, the place where I now was, must be that country which, lying between the Emperor of Morocco's dominions and the Negroes, lies waste, and uninhabited, except by wild beasts; the Negroes having abandoned it, and gone farther south, for fear of the Moors, and the Moors not thinking it worth inhabiting, by reason of its barrenness; and, indeed both forsaking it because of the prodigious numbers of tigers, lions, leopards, and other furious creatures which harbour there.

Once or twice, in the day-time, I thought I saw the Pico of Teneriffe, being the top of the mountain Teneriffe, in the Canaries, and had a great mind to venture out, in hopes of reaching thither; but having tried twice, I was forced in again by contrary winds; the sea also going too high for my little vessel; so I resolved to pursue my first design, and keep along the shore.

After this stop we made on to the southward continually, for ten or twelve days, living very sparingly on our provisions, which began to abate very much, and going no oftener into shore than we were obliged to for fresh water. My design in this, was to make the river Gambia, or Senegal; that is to say, anywhere about the Cape de Verd, where I was in hopes to meet some European ship; and if I did not, I knew not what course I had to take, but to seek for the islands or perish among the Negroes. I knew that all the ships from Europe, which sailed either to the coast of Guinea, or to Brazil, or to the East Indies, made this Cape, or those islands; and in a word I put the whole of my fortune upon this single point, either that I must meet with some ship, or must perish.

When I had pursued this resolution about ten days longer, I began to see that the land was inhabited; and in two or three places, as we sailed by, we saw people stand upon the shore to look at us; we could also perceive they were quite black and stark naked. I was once inclined to have gone on shore to them; but Xury was my better counsellor, and said to me, "No go, no go." However, I hauled in nearer the shore, that I might talk to them; and I found they ran along the shore by me a good way. I observed they had no weapons in their hands, except one, who had a long slender stick, which Xury said was a lance, and that they would throw them a great way with good aim; so I kept a distance, but talked to them by signs, as well as I could, and particularly made signs for something to eat. They beckoned to me to stop my boat, and they would fetch me some meat; upon this I lowered the top of my sail, and lay by, and two of them ran up into the country; and in less than half an hour came back, and brought with them two pieces of dry flesh and some corn, such as the produce of their country, but we neither knew what the one nor the other was; however we were willing to accept it. But how to come at it was our next dispute, for I was not for venturing on shore to them, and they were as much afraid of us; but they took a safe way for us all, for they brought it to the shore, and laid it down, and went and stood a great way off, till we fetched it on board, and then came close to us again.

We made signs of thanks to them, for we had nothing to make them amends; but an opportunity offered that very instant to oblige them wonderfully; for while we were lying by the shore, came two mighty creatures, one pursuing the other (as we took it) with great fury, from the mountains towards the sea; whether it was the male pursuing the female, or whether they were in sport or in rage, we could not tell, any more than we could tell whether it was usual or strange; but I believe it was the latter, because, in the first place, these ravenous creatures seldom appear but in the night; and, in the second place we found the people terribly frightened, especially the women. The man that had the lance, or dart, did not fly from them, but the rest did; however, as the two creatures ran directly into the water, they did not seem to offer to fall upon any of the Negroes, but plunged themselves into the sea, and swam about, as if they had come for their diversion; at last, one of them began to come nearer our boat than I at first expected; but I lay ready for him, for I had loaded my gun with all possible expedition, and bade Xury load both the others. As soon as he came fairly within my reach, I fired, and shot him directly in the head; immediately he sunk down into the water, but rose instantly, and plunged up and down, as if he was struggling for life, and so indeed he was; he immediately made to the shore; but between the wound which was his mortal hurt, and the strangling of the water, he died just before he reached the shore.

It is impossible to express the astonishment of the poor Negroes, at the noise and fire of my gun; some of them were even ready to die for fear, and fell down as dead with the very terror; but when they saw the creature dead, and sunk in the water, and that I made signs for them to come to the shore, they took heart and came to the shore, and began to search for the creature. I found him by his blood staining the water; and by the help of a rope, which I slung round him and gave the Negroes to haul, they dragged him on shore, and found that it was a most curious leopard, spotted and fine to an admirable degree; and the Negroes held up their hands with admiration, to think what it was I had killed him with.

The other creature, frightened with the flash of fire, and the noise of the gun, swam on shore, and ran up directly to the mountains from whence they came; nor could I, at that distance, know what it was. I found quickly the Negroes were for eating the flesh of this creature, so I was willing to have them take it as a favour from me; which, when I made signs to them that they might take him, they were very thankful for. Immediately they fell to work with him; and though they had no knife, yet with a sharpened piece of wood, they took off his skin as readily, and much more readily, than we could have done with a knife. They offered me some of the flesh, which I declined, making as if I would give it to them, but made signs for the skin, which they gave me very freely, and brought me a great deal more of their provisions, which, though I did not understand, yet I accepted. I then made signs to them for some water, and held out one of my jars to them, turning it bottom upwards, to show that it was empty, and that I wanted to have it filled. They called immediately to some of their friends, and there came two women, and brought a great vessel made of earth, and burnt, as I suppose, in the sun; this they set down to me, as before, and I sent Xury on shore with my jars, and filled them all three.

I was now furnished with roots and corn, such as it

was, and water; and leaving my friendly Negroes, I made forward for eleven days more, without offering to go near the shore, till I saw the land run a great length into the sea, at about the distance of four or five leagues before me; and the sea being very calm, I kept a large offing, to make this point. At length doubling the point, at about two leagues from the land, I saw plainly land on the other side, to seaward; then I concluded, as it was most certain indeed, that this was the Cape de Verd, and those the islands, called from thence, Cape de Verd Islands. However, they were at a great distance, and I could not well tell what I had best do; for if I should be taken with a gale of wind, I might reach neither.

In this dilemma, as I was very pensive, I stepped into the cabin and sat me down, Xury having the helm; when, on a sudden, the boy cried out, "Master, master, a ship with a sail!" and the foolish boy was frightened out of his wits, thinking it must needs be some of his master's ships sent to pursue us, when I knew we were gotten far enough out of their reach. I jumped out of the cabin, and immediately saw, not only the ship, but what she was, viz., that it was a Portuguese ship, and, as I thought, was bound to the Coast of Guinea, for Negroes.

With all the sail I could make, I found I should not be able to come in their way; but after I had crowded on the utmost, and began to despair, they, it seems, saw me by the help of their perspective glasses, and that it was some European boat, which, they supposed, must belong to some ship that was lost; so they shortened sail; and in about three hours' time I came up with them.

They asked me what I was in Portuguese, and in Spanish, and in French, but I understood none of them; but, at last, a Scotch sailor who was on board, called to me, and I answered him, and told him I was an Englishman, that I had made my escape out of slavery from the Moors, at Sallee; they then bade me come on board, and very kindly took me in, and all my goods.

It was an inexpressible joy to me, which any one will believe, that I was thus delivered, as I esteemed it, from such a miserable, and almost hopeless condition as I was in; and I immediately offered all I had to the captain of the ship, as a return for my deliverance; but he generously told me, he would take nothing from me, but that all I had should be delivered safe to me, when I came to the Brazils. I will carry you thither in charity, and these things will help to buy your subsistence there, and your passage home again.

SECTION IV

HE SETTLES IN THE BRAZILS AS A PLANTER—MAKES ANOTHER VOYAGE, AND IS SHIPWRECKED

As he was charitable in his proposal, so he was just in the performance, to a tittle: for he ordered the seamen, that none should offer to touch anything I had: then he took everything into his own possession, and gave me back an exact inventory of them, that I might have them, even so much as my three earthen jars.

He had a very good voyage to the Brazils, and arrived in the Bay de Todos los Santos, or All Saints' Bay, in about twenty-two days after. And now I was once more delivered from the most miserable of all conditions of life; and what to do next with myself, I was now to consider.

The generous treatment the captain gave me, I can never enough remember: he would take nothing of me for my passage, gave me twenty ducats for the leopard's skin, and forty for the lion's skin, which I had in my boat, and caused everything I had in the ship to be punctually delivered to me; and what I was willing to sell, he bought of me; such as the case of bottles, two of my guns, and a piece of the lump of bees-wax—for I had made candles of the rest; in a word, I made about two hundred and twenty pieces of eight of all my cargo; and with this stock, I went on shore in the Brazils.

I had not been long here, before I was recommended to the house of a good honest man, like himself, who had an ingenio as they call it (that is, a plantation and a sugar-house). I lived with him some time, and acquainted myself, by that means, with the manner of planting and of making sugar; and seeing how well the planters lived, and how they got rich suddenly, I resolved, if I could get a license to settle there, I would turn planter among them: endeavouring in the meantime, to find out some way to get my money, which I had left in London, remitted to me. To this purpose, getting a kind of letter of naturalisation, I purchased as much land that was uncured as my money would reach, and formed a plan for my plantation and settlement; such a one as might be suitable to the stock which I proposed to myself to receive from England.

I had a neighbour, a Portuguese of Lisbon, but born of English parents, whose name was Wells, and in much such circumstances as I was. I call him my neighbour, because his plantation lay next to mine, and we went on very sociably together. My stock was but low, as well as his; and we rather planted for food than anything else, for about two years. However, we began to increase, and our land began to come into order; so that the third year we planted some tobacco, and made each of us a large piece of ground ready for planting canes the next year.

Having lived almost four years in the Brazils, and beginning to thrive and prosper very well upon my plantation, I had not only learned the language, but had contracted an acquaintance and friendship among my fellow-planters, as well as among the merchants at St. Salvador, which was our port; and that, in my discourses among them, I had frequently given them an account of my two voyages to the coast of Guinea, the manner of trading with the Negroes there, and how easy it was to purchase on the coast for trifles—such as beads, toys, knives, scissors, hatchets, bits of glass, and the like—not only gold dust, Guinea grains, elephants' teeth, etc., but Negroes, for the service of the Brazils, in great numbers.

They listened always very attentively to my discourses on these heads, but especially to that part which related to the buying of Negroes, which was a trade, at that time, not only not far entered into, but as far as it was, had been carried on by the *assientos*, or permission of the kings of Spain and Portugal, and engrossed from the public; so that few Negroes were bought, and those excessively dear.

It happened, being in company with some merchants and planters of my acquaintance, and talking of those things very earnestly, three of them came to me the next morning, and told me they had been musing very much upon what I had discoursed with them of the last night, and they came to make a secret proposal to me; and, after enjoining me to secrecy, they told me that they had a mind to fit out a ship to go to Guinea; that they had all plantations as well as I, and were straightened for nothing so much as servants; that as it was a trade that could not be carried on, because they could not publicly sell the Negroes when they came home, so they desired to make but one voyage, to bring the Negroes on shore privately, and divide them among their own plantations; and, in a word, the question was, whether I would go as their supercargo, in the ship, to manage the trading part upon the coast of Guinea; and they offered me that I should have an equal share of the Negroes without providing any part of the stock.

I, that was born to be my own destroyer, could no more resist the offer, than I could restrain my first rambling designs. In a word, I told them I would go with all my heart, if they would undertake to look after my plantation in my absence, and would dispose of it as I should direct, if I miscarried. This they all engaged to do, and entered into writings or covenants to do so, in case of my death; making the captain of the ship that saved my life, as before, my universal heir; but obliging him to dispose of my effects as I had directed in my will; one-half of the produce being to himself, and the other to be shipped to England.

The ship being fitted out, and the cargo furnished, and all things done as by agreement, by partners in the voyage, I went on board in an evil hour again, the first of September, 1659, being the same day eight years that I went from my parents at Hull, in order to act the rebel to their authority and the fool to my own interest.

We passed the Line in about twelve days' time and were, by our last observation, in seven degrees twenty-two minutes northern latitude, when a violent tornado, or hurricane, took us quite out of our knowledge; it began from the south-east, came about to the north-west, and then settled in the north-east; from whence it blew in such a terrible manner, that for twelve days together we could do nothing but drive, and, scudding away before it, let it carry us withersoever fate and the fury of the winds directed; and, during these twelve days, I need not say that I expected every day to be swallowed up; nor, indeed, did any in the ship expect to save their lives.

About the twelfth day, the weather abating a little, the master made an observation as well as he could. He found that he had got upon the coast of Guiana, or the north part of Brazil, beyond the river Amazon, toward that of the Orinoco, commonly called the Great River; and as the ship was leaky and very much disabled he was for going back to the coast of Brazil.

I was positively against that; and looking over the charts of the sea-coast of America with him, we concluded there was no inhabited country for us to have recourse to, till we came within the circle of the Carribee islands, and therefore resolved to stand away for Barbadoes; which by keeping off to sea, to avoid the indraft of the bay or gulf of Mexico, we might easily perform, as we hoped, in about fifteen days' sail; whereas we could not possibly make our voyage to the coast of Africa, without some assistance, both to our ship and ourselves.

With this design we changed our course, and steered away N.W. by W. in order to reach some of our English islands, where I hoped for relief; but our voyage was otherwise determined; for in the latitude of twelve degrees eighteen minutes a second storm came upon us, which carried us away with the same impetuosity westward, and drove us so out of the very way of all human commerce, that had all our lives been saved, as to the sea, we stood a greater chance of being devoured by savages than ever returning to our own country.

In this distress, the wind still blowing very hard, one of our men early in the morning, cried out "Land!" and we had no sooner run out of the cabin to look out, in hopes of seeing whereabouts in the world we were, than the ship struck upon a sand, and in a moment, her motion being so stopped, the sea broke over her in such a manner, that we expected we should all have perished immediately; and we were quickly driven into our close quarters, to shelter us from the very foam and spray of the sea.

The ship having thus struck upon the sand, and sticking too fast for us to expect her getting off, we were in a dreadful condition indeed, and had nothing to do but to think of saving our lives as well as we could. We had a boat at our stern just before the storm, but she was first staved by dashing against the ship's rudder, and in the next place, she broke away, and either sunk on was driven off to sea; so there was no hope from her; we had another boat on board, but how to get her off into the sea was a doubtful thing; however, there was no room to debate, for we fancied the ship would break in pieces every minute, and some told us she was actually broken already.

In this distress, the mate of our vessel laid hold of the boat, and with the help of the rest of the men, they got her flung over the ship's side; and all getting into her, we let go, and committed ourselves, being eleven in number, to God's mercy, and the wild sea; for though the storm was abated considerably, yet the sea went dreadfully high upon the shore, and, might be well called *den wild zee*, as the Dutch call the sea in a storm.

After we had rowed, or rather driven, about a league and a half, as we reckoned it, a raging wave, mountain-like, came rolling astern of us, and plainly bade us expect the *coup de grace*. In a word, it took us with such fury that it overset the boat at once; and separating us, as well from the boat as from one another, gave us time hardly to say, "O God!" for we were all swallowed up in a moment.

Nothing can describe the confusion of thought which I felt when I sunk into the water; for though I swam very well, yet I could not deliver myself from the waves so as to draw my breath, till that wave having driven me, or rather carried me, a vast way on towards the shore, and having spent itself, went back, and left me upon the land almost dry, but half dead with the water I took in. I had so much presence of mind, as well as breath left, that seeing myself nearer the main land than I expected, I got upon my feet, and endeavoured to make on towards the land as fast as I could, before another wave should return and take me up again; but I soon found it was impossible to avoid it; for I saw the sea come after me as high as a great hill, and as furious as an enemy which I had no means or strength to contend with; my business was to hold my breath, and raise myself upon the water, if I could; and so, by swimming, to preserve my breathing, and pilot myself towards the shore, if possible; my greatest concern now being that each wave, as it would carry me a great way towards the shore when it came on might not carry back again with it when it gave back towards the sea.

The wave that came upon me again buried me at once twenty or thirty feet deep in its own body; and I could feel myself carried with a mighty force and swiftness towards the shore, a very great way; but I held my breath, and assisted myself to swim still forward with all my might. I was ready to burst with holding my breath, when, as I felt myself rising up, so, to my immediate relief, I found my head and hands shoot out above the surface of the water; and though it was not two seconds of time that I could keep myself so, yet it relieved me greatly, gave me breath and new courage. I was covered again with water a good while, but not so long but I held it out; and finding the water had spent itself, and began to return I struck forward against the return of the waves, and felt ground again with my feet. I stood still a few moments, to recover breath, and till the water went from me and then took to my heels, and ran with what strength I had farther towards the shore. But neither would this deliver me from the fury of the sea, which came pouring in after me, again; and twice more I was lifted up by the waves and carried forwards as before, the shore being very flat.

The last time of these two had well nigh been fatal to me; for the sea, having hurried me along, as before, landed me, or rather dashed me, against a piece of rock, and with such force, that it left me senseless, and indeed helpless, as to my own deliverance; for the blow, taking my side and breast, beat the breath, as it were, quite out of my body; and had it returned again immediately, I must have been strangled in the water; but I recovered a little before the return of the waves, and, seeing I should again be covered with the water, I resolved to hold fast by a piece of rock, and so to hold my breath, if possible, till the wave went back. Now as the waves were not so high, as the first, being nearer land, I held my hold till the wave abated, and then fetched another run, which brought me so near the shore, that the next wave, though it went over me, yet did not so swallow me up as to carry me away; and the next run I took, I got to the main land; where, to my great comfort, I clambered up the cliffs of the shore, and sat me down upon the grass, free from danger, and quite out of the reach of the water.

I was now landed, and safe on shore; and began to look up and thank God that my life was saved, in a case wherein there was, some minutes before, scarcely any room to hope.

I walked about on the shore, lifting up my hands, and my whole being, as I may say, wrapped up in the contemplation of my deliverance; making a thousand gestures and motions, which I cannot describe; reflecting upon my comrades that were drowned, and that there should not be one saved but myself; for, as for them, I never saw them afterwards, or any sign of them, except three of their hats, one cap, and two shoes that were not fellows.

I cast my eyes to the stranded vessel—when the breach and froth of the sea being so big I could hardly see it, it lay so far off—and "considered Lord! how was it possible I could get on shore?"

I began to look around me to see what kind of a place I was in, and what was next to be done; and I soon found my comforts abate, and that, in a word, I had a dreadful deliverance; for I was wet, had no clothes to shift me, nor anything either to eat or drink, to comfort me; neither did I see any prospect before me, but that of perishing with hunger, or being devoured by wild beasts; and that which was particularly afflicting to me was, that I had no weapon either to hunt and kill any creature for my sustenance, or to defend myself against any other creatures that might desire to kill me for theirs. In a word, I had nothing about me but a knife, a tobacco-pipe, and a little tobacco. Night coming upon me, I began, with a heavy heart, to consider what would be my lot if there were any ravenous beasts in that country.

All the remedy that offered to my thoughts, was, to get up into a thick bushy tree. I walked about a furlong from the shore to see if I could find any fresh water; which I did, to my great joy; and having drunk, and put a little tobacco into my mouth to prevent hunger, I went to the tree, and getting up into it, endeavoured to place myself so as that if I should fall asleep, I might not fall; and having cut me a stick, for my defence, I took up my lodging; and having been excessively fatigued, I fell asleep, and slept as comfortable as, I believe, few could have done in my condition; and found myself much refreshed.

SECTION V

ROBINSON FINDS HIMSELF IN A DESOLATE ISLAND—PROCURES A STOCK OF ARTICLES FROM THE WRECK—CONSTRUCTS HIS HABITATION

When I woke it was broad day, the weather clear, and the storm abated, so that the sea did not rage and swell as before; but that which surprised me most was, that the ship was lifted off in the night from the sand where she lay, by the swelling of the tide, and was driven up almost as far as the rock which I at first mentioned, where I had been so bruised by the wave dashing me against it. This being within about a mile from the shore where I was, and the ship seeming to stand upright still, I wished myself on board, that at least I might save some necessary things for my use.

When I came down from my apartment in the tree, I looked about me again, and the first thing I found was the boat; which lay, as the wind and sea had tossed her up, upon the land, about two miles on my right hand. I walked as far as I could upon the shore to have got to her; but found a neck, or inlet, of water, between me and the boat, which was about half-a-mile broad; so I came back for the present, being more intent upon getting at the ship, where I had hoped to find something for my present subsistence.

A little after noon, I found the sea very calm, and the tide ebbed so far out, that I could come within a quarter of a mile of the ship: and here I found a fresh renewing of my grief; for I saw evidently, that if we had kept on board, we had been all safe; that is to say, we had all got safe on shore, and had not been so miserable as to be left entirely destitute of all comfort and company, as I now was. This forced tears from my eyes again; but as there was little relief in that, I resolved, if possible, to get to the ship; so I pulled off my clothes, for the weather was hot to extremity, and took to the water: but when I came to the ship, my difficulty was still greater to know how to get on board: for as she lay aground, and high out of the water, there was nothing in my reach to lay hold of. I swam round her twice, and the second time I spied a small piece of rope, which I wondered I did not see at first, hang down by the forechains so low, as that with great difficulty I got hold of it, and by the help of that rope got into the forecastle of the ship. Here I found that the ship was bilged, and had a great deal of water in her hold; but that she lay so on the side of a bank of hard sand, or rather earth, that her stern lay lifted up upon the bank, and her head low, almost to the water. By this means all her quarter was free, and all that was in that part was dry; for you may be sure my first work was to search and to see what was spoiled and what was free: and, first I found that all the ship's provisions were dry and untouched by the water; and being very well disposed to eat, I went to the bread-room, and filled my pockets with biscuit, and ate it as I went about other things, for I had no time to lose. I also found some rum in the great cabin, of which I took a large dram, and which I had indeed need enough of, to spirit me for what was before me. Now I wanted nothing but a boat, to furnish myself with many things which I foresaw would be very necessary to me.

It was in vain to sit still and wish for what was not to be had, and this extremity roused my application; we had several spare yards, and two or three large spars of wood, and a spare topmast or two in the ship; I resolved to fall to work with these, and flung as many overboard as I could manage for their weight, tying every one with a rope, that they might not drive away. When this was done, I went down the ship's side, and pulling them to me, I tied four of them fast together at both ends, as well as I could, in the form of a raft, and laying two or three short pieces of plank upon them, crossways, I found I could walk upon it very well, but that it was not able to bear any great weight, the pieces being too light; so I went to work, and with the carpenter's saw I cut a spare topmast into three lengths, and added them to my raft, with a great deal of labour and pains. But the hope of furnishing myself with necessaries, encouraged me to go beyond what I should have been able to have done upon another occasion.

My raft was now strong enough to bear any reasonable weight. My next care was what to load it with, and how to preserve what I laid upon it from the surf of the sea; but I was not long considering this. I first laid all the planks or boards upon it that I could get, and having considered well what I most wanted, I got three of the seamen's chests which I had broken open and emptied and lowered them down upon my raft; these I filled with provisions, viz., bread, rice, three Dutch cheeses, five pieces of dried goat's flesh (which we lived much upon), and a little remainder of European corn, which had been laid by for some fowls which we had brought to sea with us, but the fowls were killed. There had been some barley and wheat together, but, to my great disappointment, I found afterwards that the rats had eaten or spoiled it all. As for liquors, I found several cases of bottles belonging to our skipper, in which were some cordial waters; and, in all, five or six gallons of rack. These I stowed by themselves, there being no need to put them into the chests, nor any room for them. While I was doing this, I found the tide began to flow, though very calm, and I had the mortification to see my coat, shirt, and waistcoat, which I had left on shore, upon the sand, swim away; as for my breeches, which were only linen and open-kneed, I swam on board in them, and my stockings. However, this put me rummaging for clothes, of which I found enough, but took no more than I wanted for present use, for I had other things which my eye was more upon; as, first, tools to work with on shore: and it was after long searching that I found the carpenter's chest, which was indeed a very useful prize to me, and much more valuable than a ship-lading of gold would have been at that time. I got it down to my raft, even whole as it was, without losing time to look into it, for I knew in general what it contained.

My next care was for some ammunition and arms. There were two very good fowling-pieces in the great cabin, and two pistols; these I secured first, with some powder-horns and a small bag of shot, and two old rusty swords. I knew there were three barrels of powder in the ship, but knew not where our gunner had stowed them; but with much search I found them, two of them dry and good, the third had taken water. Those two I got on my raft, with the arms. And now I thought myself pretty well freighted, and began to think how I should get on shore with them, having neither sail, oar, nor rudder; and the least capful of wind would have overset all my navigation. I hoped to find some creek or river which I might make use of as a port to get to land with my cargo.

As I imagined; so it was; there appeared before me a little opening of the land, and I found a strong current of the tide set into it; so I guided my raft, as well as I could, to get into the middle of the stream. But here I had like to have suffered a second shipwreck, which if I had, I think it verily would have broken my heart; for, knowing nothing of the coast, my raft ran aground at one end of it upon a shoal, and, not being aground at the other end, it wanted but a little that all my cargo had slipped off toward the end that was afloat, and so fallen into the water. I did my utmost, by setting my back against the chests, to keep them in their places, but could not thrust off the raft with all my strength; neither durst I stir from the posture I was in, but holding up the chests with all my might, I stood in that manner near half an hour, in which time the rising of the water brought me a little more upon a level; and a little after, the water still rising, my raft floated again, and I thrust her off with the oar I had into the channel, and then driving up higher, I at length found myself in the mouth of a little river, with land on both sides, and a strong current or tide running up. I looked on both sides for a proper place to get to shore, for I was not willing to be driven too high up the river; hoping, in time, to see some ship at sea, and therefore resolved to place myself as near the coast as I could.

At length I spied a little cove on the right shore of the creek, to which, with great pain and difficulty, I guided my raft, and at last got so near, as that, reaching ground with my oar, I could thrust her directly in; but here I had like to have tipped all my cargo into the sea again; for that shore lying pretty steep, that is to say, sloping, there was no place to land, but where one end of my float, if it ran on shore, would lie so high, and the other sink lower, as before, that it would endanger my cargo again. All that I could do was to wait till the tide was at the highest, keeping the raft with my oar like an anchor, to hold the side of it fast to the shore, near a flat piece of ground, which I expected the water would flow over; and so it did. As soon as I found water enough, for my raft drew about a foot of water, I thrust her upon that flat piece of ground, and there fastened or moored her, by sticking my two broken oars into the ground, one on one side, near the end, and one on the other side, near the other end: and thus I lay till the water ebbed away, and left my raft and all my cargo safe on shore.

My next work was to view the country, and seek a proper place for my habitation and where to stow my goods, to secure them from whatever might happen. Where I was I yet knew not; whether on the continent, or on an island; whether inhabited, or not inhabited: whether in danger of wild beasts, or not. There was a hill, not above a mile from me, which rose up very steep and high, and which seemed to overtop some other hills, which lay as in a ridge from it, northward. I took out one of the fowling pieces, and one of the pistols, and a horn of powder; and thus armed, I travelled for discovery up to the top of that hill; where, after I had, with great labour and difficulty, got up to the top, I saw my fate, to my great affliction, viz., that I was on an island, environed in every way with the sea, no land to be seen, except some rocks, which lay a great way off, and two small islands, less than this, which lay about three leagues to the west.

I found also that the island I was on was barren, and as I saw good reason to believe, uninhabited, except by wild beasts, of whom, however, I saw none; yet I saw abundance of fowls, but knew not their kinds; neither, when I killed them, could I tell what was fit for food, and what not. At my coming back, I shot at a great bird, which I saw sitting upon a tree, on the side of a great wood. I believe it was the first gun that had been fired there since the creation of the world; I had no sooner fired, but from all parts of the wood there arose an innumerable number of fowls, of many sorts, making a confused screaming, and crying, every one according to his usual note; but not one of them of any kind that I knew. As for the creature I killed, I took it to be a kind of hawk, its colour and beak resembling it, but it had no talons or claws more than common. Its flesh was carrion and fit for nothing.

I now began to consider that I might yet get a great many things out of the ship, which would be useful to me, and particularly some of the rigging and sails, and such other things as might come to land; and I resolved to make another voyage on board the vessel, if possible. And as I knew that the first storm that blew must necessarily break her all in pieces, I resolved to set all other things apart, till I got everything out of the ship that I could get. Then I called a council, that is to say, in my thoughts, whether I should take back the raft; but this appeared impracticable: so I resolved to go as before, when the tide was down; and I did so, only that I stripped before I went from my hut; having nothing on but a chequered shirt, a pair of linen drawers, and a pair of pumps on my feet.

I got on board the ship as before, and prepared a second raft; and having had experience of the first, I neither made this so unwieldy, or loaded it so hard, but yet I brought away several things very useful to me; as, first, in the carpenter's stores, I found two or three bags of nails and spikes, a great screw-jack, a dozen or two of hatchets; and, above all, that most useful thing a grindstone. All these I secured together, with several things belonging to the gunner; particularly, two or three iron crows, and two barrels of musket bullets, seven muskets, and another fowling-piece, with some small quantity of powder more; a large bag full of small shot, and a great roll of sheet lead; but this last was so heavy, I could not hoist it up to get it over the ship's side. Beside, these things, I took all the men's clothes that I could find, and a spare fore-top-sail, a hammock, and some bedding; and with this I loaded my second raft, and brought them all safe on shore, to my very great comfort.

Having got my second cargo on shore—though I was fain to open the barrels of powder, and bring them by parcels for they were too heavy, being large casks—I went to work to make a little tent, with the sails and some poles which I cut for that purpose; and into this tent I brought everything that I knew would spoil either with rain or sun; and I piled all the empty chests and casks up in a circle round the tent, to fortify it from any sudden attempt either from man or beast.

When I had done this, I blocked up the door of the tent with boards within, and an empty chest set up on end without; and spreading one of the beds upon the ground, laying my two pistols just at my head, and my gun at length by me, I went to bed for the first time, and slept very quietly all night, for I was very weary and heavy; for the night before I had slept little, and had laboured very hard all day, as well to fetch all those things from the ship, and to get them on shore.

I had the biggest magazine of all kinds now that ever was laid up, I believe, for one man; but I was not satisfied still; for while the ship sat upright in that posture, I thought I ought to get everything out of her that I could; so every day, at low water, I went on board, and brought away something or other: but particularly the third time I went, I brought away as much of the rigging as I could, as also all the small ropes and rope-twine I could get, with a piece of square canvas, which was to mend the sails upon occasion, and the barrel of wet gunpowder. In a word, I brought away all the sails first and last; only that I was fain to cut them in pieces, and bring as much at a time as I could; for they were no more useful to be sails, but as mere canvas only.

But that which comforted me still more, was, that, last of all, after I had made five or six such voyages as these, and thought I had nothing more to expect from the ship that was worth my meddling with; I say, after all this, I found a great hogshead of bread, and three large runlets of rum or spirits, and a box of sugar, and a barrel of fine flour; this was surprising to me, because I had given over expecting any more provisions, except what was spoiled by the water. I soon emptied the hogshead of that bread, and wrapped it up, parcel by parcel, in pieces of the sails, which I cut out; and, in a word, I got all this safe on shore also.

The next day I made another voyage, and now having plundered the ship of what was portable and fit to hand out, I began with the cables, and cutting the great cable into pieces such as I could move, I got two cables and a hawser on shore, with all the ironwork I could get; and having cut down the spritsail-yard, and the mizen-yard, and everything I could, to make a large raft, I loaded it with all those heavy goods, and came away; but my good luck now began to leave me; for this raft was so unwieldy, and so overladen, that after I was entered the little cover, where I had landed the rest of my goods, not being able to guide it so handily as I did the other, it overset, and threw me and all my cargo into the water; as for myself it was no great harm, for I was near the shore; but as to my cargo, it was a great part of it lost, especially the iron, which I expected would have been of great use to me: however, when the tide was out, I got most of the pieces of cable ashore, and some of the iron, though with infinite labour; for I was fain to go for it into the water, a work which fatigued me very much. After this I went every day on board, and brought away what I could get.

I had been now thirteen days ashore, and had been eleven times on board the ship; in which time I had brought away all that one pair of hands could well be supposed capable to bring: though I believe verily, had the calm weather held, I should have brought away the whole ship, piece by piece, but preparing the twelfth time, to go on board, I found the wind began to rise: however, at low water, I went on board; and though I thought I had rummaged the cabin so effectually, as that nothing could be found, yet I discovered a locker with drawers in it, in one of which I found two or three razors, and one pair of large scissors, with some ten or a dozen of good knives and forks; in another I found about thirty-six pounds in money, some European coin, some Brazil, some pieces of eight, some gold, and some silver.

I smiled to myself at the sight of this money; "O drug!" I exclaimed, "what art thou good for? Thou art not worth to me, no, not the taking off the ground; one of those knives is worth all this heap: I have no manner of use for thee; e'en remain where thou art, and go to the bottom, as a creature whose life is not worth saving." However, upon second thoughts, I took it away; and wrapping all this in a piece of canvas, I began to think of making another raft; but while I was preparing this, I found the sky overcast, and the wind began to rise, and in a quarter of an hour it blew a fresh gale from the shore. It presently occurred to me, that it was in vain to pretend to make a raft with the wind offshore, and that it was my business to be gone before the tide of flood began, or otherwise I might not be able to reach the shore at all. Accordingly I let myself down into the water, and swam across the channel which lay between the ship and the sands, and even that with difficulty enough, partly with the weight of the things I had about me, and partly the roughness of the water; for the wind rose very hastily, and before it was quite high water it blew a storm.

But I was got home to my little tent, where I lay, with all my wealth about me very secure. It blew very hard all that night, and in the morning, when I looked out, behold no more ship was to be seen! I was a little surprised, but recovered myself with this satisfactory reflection, viz., that I had lost no time, nor abated no diligence, to get everything out of her that could be useful to me, and that, indeed, there was little left in her that I was able to bring away, if I had had more time.

I now gave over any more thoughts of the ship, or of anything out of her, except what might drive on shore, from her wreck; as, indeed, divers pieces of her afterwards did; but those things were of small use to me.

My thoughts were now wholly employed about securing myself either against savages, if any should appear, or wild beasts, if any were on the island; and I had many thoughts of the method how to do this, and what kind of dwelling to make, whether I should make a cave in the earth, or a tent upon the earth; and, in short, I resolved upon both; the manner and description of which, it may not be improper to give an account of.

I soon found the place I was in was not for my settlement, particularly because it was upon a low, moorish ground, near the sea, and I believed it would not be wholesome; and more particularly because there was no fresh water near it: so I resolved to find a more healthy and convenient spot of ground.

I consulted several things in my situation, which I found would be proper for me; first, air and fresh water, I just now mentioned: secondly, shelter from the heat of the sun; thirdly, security from ravenous creatures, whether men or beasts; fourthly, a view to the sea, that if God sent any ship in sight, I might not lose any advantage for my deliverance, of which I was not willing to banish all my expectation yet.

In search for a proper place for this, I found a little plain on the side of a rising hill, whose front towards this little plain was as steep as a house-side, so that nothing could come down upon me from the top. On the side of this rock, there was a hollow place, worn a little way in, like the entrance or door of a cave; but there was not really any cave, or way into the rock, at all.

On the flat of the green, just before this hollow place, I resolved to pitch my tent. This plain was not above one hundred yards broad, and about twice as long, and lay like a green before my door; and, at the end of it, descended irregularly every way down into the low ground by the sea-side. It was on the N.N.W. side of the hill; so that it was sheltered from the heat every day, till it came to a W. and by S. sun or thereabouts, which, in those countries, is near the setting.

Before I set up my tent, I drew a half-circle before the hollow-place, which took in about ten yards in its semi-diameter, from the rock, and twenty yards in its diameter, from its beginning and ending.

In this half-circle I pitched two rows of strong stakes, driving them into the ground till they stood very firm like piles, the biggest end being out of the ground, about five feet and a half, and sharpened on the top. The two rows did not stand above six inches from one another.

Then I took the pieces of cable which I cut in the ship and laid them in rows, one upon another, within the circle, between these two rows of stakes, up to the top, placing other stakes in the inside, leaning against them, about two feet and a half high like a spur to a post; and this fence was so strong, that neither man nor beast could get into it or over it. This cost me a great deal of time and labour, especially to cut the piles in the woods, bring them to the place, and drive them into the earth.

The entrance into this place I made to be not by a door, but by a short ladder to go over the top; which ladder, when I was in, I lifted over after me; and so I was completely fenced in and fortified, as I thought, from all the world, and consequently slept secure in the night, which otherwise

I could not have done; though, as it appeared afterwards, there was no need for all this caution against the enemies that I apprehended danger from.

SECTION VI

CARRIES ALL HIS RICHES, PROVISIONS, ETC., INTO HIS HABITATION—DREARINESS OF SOLITUDE—CONSOLATORY REFLECTIONS

INTO this fence, or fortress, with infinite labour, I carried all my riches, all my provisions, ammunition, and stores, of which you have the account above; and I made a large tent, which, to preserve me from the rains, that in one part of the year are very violent there, I made double, viz., one smaller tent within, and one larger tent above it, and covered the uttermost with a large tarpaulin, which I had saved among the sails.

And now I lay no more for a while in the bed which I had brought on shore, but in a hammock, which was indeed a very good one, and belonged to the mate of the ship.

Into this tent I brought all my provisions, and everything that would spoil by the wet; and having thus enclosed all my goods, I made up the entrance, which till now I had left open, and so passed and repassed, as I said, by a short ladder.

When I had done this I began to work my way into the rock, and bringing all the earth and stones that I dug down out through my tent, I laid them up within my fence in the nature of a terrace, so that it raised the ground within about a foot and a half; and thus I made me a cave, just behind my tent, which served me like a cellar to my house. It cost me much labour and many days, before all these things were brought to perfection; and therefore, I must go back to some other things which took up some of my thoughts. At the same time it happened, after I had laid my scheme, for the setting up of my tent, and making the cave, that a storm of rain falling from a thick, dark cloud, a sudden flash of lightning happened, and after that, a great clap of thunder, as is naturally the effect of it. I was not so much surprised with the lightning as I was with a thought which darted into my mind as swift as the lightning itself: O my powder! My very heart sank within me when I thought, that at one blast all my powder might be destroyed; on which not my defence only, but the providing me food, as I thought, entirely depended. I was nothing near so anxious about my own danger, though, had the powder taken fire, I should never have known who had hurt me.

Such impressions did this make upon me, that after the storm was over, I laid aside all my works, my building and fortifying and applied myself to make bags and boxes to separate the powder, and to keep it a little and a little in a parcel, in hope that whatever might come, it might not all take fire at once; and to keep it so apart that it should not be possible to make one part fire another. I finished this work in about a fortnight; and I think my powder, which in all was about two hundred and forty pounds weight, was divided into not less than a hundred parcels. As to the barrel that had been wet, I did not apprehend any danger from that; so I placed it in my new cave, which, in my fancy, I called my kitchen, and the rest I hid up and down in holes among the rocks, so that no wet might come to it, marking very carefully where I laid it.

In the interval of time while this was doing, I went out at least once every day with my gun. One day I killed a she-goat, which had a little kid by her, which she gave suck to, which grieved me heartily; but when the old one fell, the kid stood stock still by her, till I came and took her up; and not only so, but when I carried the old one with me upon my shoulders, the kid followed me quite to my enclosure; upon which I laid down the dam, and took the kid in my arms, and carried it over my pale, in hopes to have bred it up tame; but it would not eat; so I was forced to kill it, and eat it myself. These two supplied me with flesh a great while, for I ate sparingly, and preserved my provisions (my bread especially) as much as I possibly could.

And now being about to enter into a melancholy relation of a scene of silent life, such perhaps, as was never heard of in the world before, I shall take it from its beginning, and continue it in its order. It was, by my account, the 30th of September, when, in the manner as above said, I first set foot upon this horrid island; when the sun being to us in its autumnal equinox, was almost just over my head: for I reckoned myself, by observation, to be in the latitude of nine degrees twenty-two minutes north of the Line.

SECTION VII

ROBINSON'S MODE OF RECKONING TIME—DIFFICULTIES ARISING FROM WANT OF TOOLS—HE ARRANGES HIS HABITATION

AFTER I had been there about ten or twelve days, it came into my thoughts that I should lose my reckoning of time for want of books, and pen and ink, and should even forget the Sabbath days from the working days: but, to prevent this, I cut it with my knife into a large post, in capital letters; and making it into a great cross, I set it up on the shore where I first landed, viz., "I came on shore here on the 30th of September, 1659." Upon the sides of this square post I cut every day a notch with my knife, and every seventh notch was as long again as the rest, and every first day of the month as long again as that long one: and thus I kept my calendar, or weekly, monthly, and yearly reckoning of time.

But it happened, that among the many things which I brought out of the ship, in the several voyages which, as above mentioned, I made to it, I got several things of less value, but not at all less useful to me, which I found some time after, in rummaging the chests: as in particular, pens, ink, and paper; several parcels in the captain's, mate's, gunner's, and carpenter's keeping; three or four compasses, some mathematical instruments, dials, perspectives, charts, and books of navigation; all of which I huddled together, whether I might want them or no: also I found three very good Bibles, which came to me in my cargo from England, and which I had packed up among my things; some Portuguese books also, and, among them, two or three popish prayer-books, and several other books, all which I carefully secured. And I must not forget, that we had in the ship a dog, and two cats, of whose eminent history I may have occasion to say something, in its place; for I carried both the cats with me; and as for the dog he jumped out of the ship himself, and swam on shore the day after I went on shore with my first cargo, and was a trusty servant to me for many years; I wanted nothing that he could fetch me, nor any company that he could make up to me, I only wanted to have him talk to me, but that he could not do. As I observed before. I found pens, ink, and paper, and I husbanded them to the utmost; and I shall show that while my ink lasted, I kept things very exact, but after that was gone I could not; for I could not make any ink by any means that I could devise.

And this put me in mind that I wanted many things, notwithstanding all that I had amassed together; and of these, this of ink was one; as also a spade, pickaxe, and shovel, to dig or remove the earth; needles, pins, and thread; as for linen, I soon learned to want that without much difficulty.

This want of tools made every work I did go on heavily: and it was nearly a whole year before I had entirely finished my little pale, or surrounded my habitation. The piles or stakes, which were as heavy as I could well lift, were a long time in cutting and preparing in the woods, and more by far in bringing home; so that I spent sometimes two days in cutting and bringing home one of those posts, and a third in driving it into the ground; for which purpose, I got a heavy piece of wood at first, but at last bethought me of one of the iron crows; which, however, though I found it answer, made driving these posts or piles very laborious and tedious work. But what need I have been concerned at the tediousness of anything I had to do, seeing I had time enough to do it in; nor had I any other employment, if that had been over, at least that I could foresee, except the ranging the island to seek for food; which I did more or less, every day.

I have already described my habitation, which was a tent under the side of a rock, surrounded with a strong pale of posts and cables; but I might now rather call it a wall, for I raised a kind of wall against it of turfs, about two feet thick on the outside: and after some time (I think it was a year and half) I raised rafters from it, leaning to the rock, and thatched or covered it with boughs of trees, and such things as I could get, to keep out the rain; which I found, at some times of the year, very violent.

I have already observed how I brought all my goods into this pale, and into the cave which I had made behind me.

But I must observe, too, that at first this was a confused heap of goods, which, as they lay in no order, so they took up all my place; I had no room to turn myself: so I set myself to enlarge my cave, and work further into the earth; for it was a loose sandy rock, which yielded easily to the labour I bestowed upon it; and when I found I was pretty safe as to the beasts of prey, I worked sideways, to the right hand, into the rock, and then turning to the right again, worked quite out, and made me a door to come out in the outside of my pale or fortification.

This gave me not only egress and regress, as it were a back way to my tent and to my storehouse, but gave me room to stow my goods.

And now I began to apply myself to make such necessary things as I found I most wanted, particularly a chair and a table; for without these I was not able to enjoy the few comforts I had in the world; I could not write, or eat, or do several things with so much pleasure, without a table; so I went to work. And here I must need observe, that as reason is the substance and original of mathematics, so that by stating and squaring everything by reason, and by making the most rational judgment of things, every man may be, in time, master of every mechanic art. I had never handled a tool in my life; and yet, in time, by labour, application, and contrivance I found at last that I wanted nothing but I could have made, especially if I had had tools. However, I made abundance of things, even without tools: and some with no more tools than an adze and a hatchet, which perhaps were never made that way before, and that with infinite labour. For example, if I wanted a board, I had no other way but to cut down a tree, set it on an edge before me, and hew it flat on either side with my axe, till I had brought it to be as thin as a plank, and then dub it smooth with my adze. It is true, by this method, I could make but one board of a whole tree; but this I had no remedy for but patience, any more than I had for a prodigious deal of time and labour which it took me up to make a plank or board: but my time or labour was little worth, and so it was as well employed one way as another.

I made me a table and a chair, in the first place; and this I did out of short pieces of boards that I brought on my raft from the ship. But when I wrought out some boards, as above, I made large shelves, of the breadth of a foot and a half, one over another, all along one side of my cave, to lay all my tools, nails, and iron work on; and, in a word, to separate every thing at large in their places, that I might easily come at them. I knocked pieces into the wall of the rock, to hang my guns, and all things that would hang up; so that had my cave been seen, it looked like a general magazine of all necessary things; and I had every thing so ready at my hand, that it was a great pleasure to me to see all my goods in such order, and especially to find my stock of all necessaries so great.

And now it was that I began to keep a journal of every day's employment; for, indeed, at first, I was of too much hurry, and not only as to labour, but in much discomposure of mind; and my journal would, too, have been full of many dull things.

Some days after this, and after I have been on board the ship and got all that I could out of her, I could not forbear getting up to the top of a little mountain, and looking out to sea, in hopes of seeing a ship: then fancy that, at a vast distance, I spied a sail, please myself with hopes of it, and, after looking steadily, till I was almost blind, lose it quite, and sit down and weep like a child, and thus increase my misery by my folly.

But having got over these things in some measure, and having settled my household stuff and habitation, made me a table and a chair, and all about me as handsome as I could, I began to keep my journal: of which I shall here give you the copy (though in it will be told all these particulars over again) as long as it lasted; for, having no more ink, I was forced to leave it off.

SECTION VIII

ROBINSON'S JOURNAL—DETAILS OF HIS DOMESTIC ECONOMY AND CONTRIVANCES—SHOCK OF AN EARTHQUAKE

THE JOURNAL

SEPTEMBER 30, 1659.—I, poor miserable Robinson Crusoe, being shipwrecked, during a dreadful storm, in the offing, came on shore on this dismal, unfortunate island, which I called the ISLAND OF DESPAIR; all the rest of the ship's company being drowned, and myself almost dead.

October 1.—In the morning I saw, to my great surprise, the ship had floated with the high tide, and was driven on shore again much nearer the island. I hoped, if the wind abated, I might get on board, and get some food and necessaries out of her for my relief. I spent great part of this day in perplexing myself on these things; but at length, seeing the ship almost dry, I went upon the sand as near as I could, and then swam on board. This day also it continued raining, though with no wind at all.

From the 1st of October to the 24th. All these days entirely spent in many several voyages to get all I could out of the ship; which I brought on shore, every tide of flood, upon rafts. Much rain also in these days, though with some intervals of fair weather: but it seems this was the rainy season.

Oct. 25.—It rained all night and all day, with some gusts of wind; during which time the ship broke in pieces (the wind blowing a little harder than before) and was no more to be seen, except the wreck of her, and that only at low water. I spent this day in covering and securing the goods which I had saved, that the rain might not spoil them.

From the 26th to the 30th, I worked very hard in carrying all my goods to my habitation, though some part of the time it rained exceedingly hard.

The 31st, in the morning, I went out into the island with my gun, to see for some food, and discover the country; when I killed a she-goat, and her kid followed me home which I afterwards killed also, because it would not feed.

November 1.—I set up my tent under a rock, and lay there for the first night; making it as large as I could, with stakes driven in to swing my hammock upon.

Nov. 4.—This morning I began to order my times of work of going out with my gun, time to sleep, and time of diversion; viz., every morning I walked out with my gun for two or three hours, if it did not rain; then employed myself to work till about eleven o'clock; then eat what I had to live on; and from twelve to two I lay down to sleep, the weather being excessively hot; and then, in the evening, to work again. The working part of this day and the next was wholly employed in making my table, for I was as yet but a very sorry workman: though time and necessity made me a complete natural mechanic soon after as I believe they would any one else.

Nov. 13.—This day it rained; which refreshed me exceedingly, and cooled the earth: but it was accompanied with terrible thunder and lightning, which frightened me dreadfully, for fear of my powder. As soon as it was over I resolved to separate my stock of powder into as many little parcels as possible, that it might not be in danger.

Nov. 17.—This day I began to dig behind my tent, into the rock, to make room for any further convenience.

NOTE.—Three things I wanted exceedingly for this work, viz., a pickaxe, a shovel, and a wheelbarrow, or basket: so I desisted from my work and began to consider how to supply these wants, and make me some tools. As for pickaxe, I made use of the iron crows, which were proper enough, though heavy: but the next thing was a shovel or spade; this was so absolutely necessary, that, indeed, I could do nothing effectually without it; but what kind of one to make I knew not.

Nov. 18.—The next day, in searching the woods, I found a tree of that wood, or like it, which, in the Brazils, they call the iron tree, from its exceeding hardness: of this, with great labour, and almost spoiling my axe, I cut a piece; and brought it home, too, with difficulty enough, for it was exceeding heavy. The excessive hardness of the wood, and my having no other way, made me a long while upon this machine: for I worked it effectually by little and little, into the form of a shovel or spade; the handle exactly shaped like ours in England only that the board part having no iron shod upon it at the bottom, it would not last me so long; however, it served well enough for the uses which I had occasion to put it to; but never was a shovel, I believe, made after that fashion or so long in making.

Nov. 23.—My other work having now stood still, because of my making these tools, when they were finished I went on; and working every day, as my strength and time allowed, I spent eighteen days entirely in widening and deepening my cave, that it might hold my goods commodiously.

December 10.—I began now to think my cave or vault

finished; when on a sudden (it seems I had made it too large) a great quantity of earth fell down from the top and one side; so much, that, in short, it frightened me, and not without reason too; for if I had been under it, I should never have wanted a grave-digger. Upon this disaster, I had a great deal of work to do over again, for I had the loose earth to carry out; and, which was of more importance, I had the ceiling to prop up, so that I might be sure no more would come down.

Dec. 11.—This day I went to work with it accordingly; and got two shores or posts pitched upright to the top, with two pieces of board across over each post; this I finished the next day; and setting more posts up with boards, in about a week more I had the roof secured; and the posts standing in rows, served me for partitions to part off my house.

Dec. 17.—From this day to the 20th, I placed shelves, and knocked up nails on the posts, to hang everything up that could be hung up; and now I began to be in some order within doors.

Dec. 20.—I carried everything into the cave, and began to furnish my house, and set up some pieces of boards, like a dresser, to order my victuals upon; but boards began to be very scarce with me; also I made me another table.

Dec. 28, 29, 30, 31.—Great heats and no breeze; so that there was no stirring abroad, except in the evening, for food; this time I spent in putting all my things in order within doors.

January 1.—Very hot still; but I went abroad early and late with my gun, and lay still in the middle of the day. This evening, going further into the valleys which lay towards the centre of the island, I found there were plenty of goats, though exceedingly shy, and hard to come at; however, I resolved to try if I could not bring my dog to hunt them down. Accordingly, the next day, I went with my dog, and set him upon the goats: but I was mistaken, for they all faced about upon the dog: and he knew his danger too well, for he would not come near them.

Jan. 3.—I began my fence or wall; which, being still jealous of my being attacked by somebody, I resolved to make very thick and strong.

During this time, I made my rounds in the woods for game every day when the rain permitted me, and made frequent discoveries, in these walks, of something or other to my advantage; particularly, I found a kind of wild pigeons, who built not as wood-pigeons, in a tree, but rather as house-pigeons, in the holes of the rocks; and, taking some young ones, I endeavoured to breed them up tame, and did so; but when they grew older, they flew all away; which, perhaps, was, at first, for want of feeding them, for I had nothing to give them; however, I frequently found their nests, and got their young ones, which were very good meat. In the middle of all my labours it happened, that in rummaging my things I found a little bag; which, as I hinted before, had been filled with corn, for the feeding of poultry; not for this voyage, but before, as I suppose, when the ship came from Lisbon. What little remainder of corn had been in the bag was all devoured by the rats, and I saw nothing in the bag but husks and dust: and being willing to have the bag for some other use (I think it was to put powder in, when I divided it for fear of the lightning, or some such use), I shook the husks of corn out of it, on one side of my fortification, under the rock.

It was a little before the great rain now mentioned, that I threw this stuff away; taking no notice of anything, and not so much as remembering that I had thrown anything there: when, about a month after, I saw some few stalks of something green shooting out of the ground, which I fancied might be some plant I had not seen; but I was surprised, and perfectly astonished, when, after a longer time, I saw about ten or twelve ears come out, which were perfect green barley, of the same kind as our European, nay, of our English barley.

I at first thought these the pure productions of providence for my support; and, not doubting that there was more in the place, I went over all that part of the island where I had been before, searching in every corner, and under every rock, for more of it, but I could not find any. At last it occurred to my thoughts, that I had shaken out a bag of chickens meat in that place, then the wonder began to cease; and I must confess, my religious thankfulness to God's providence began to abate, too, upon the discovering that all this was nothing but what was common; though I ought to have been as thankful for so strange and unforeseen a providence, as if it had been miraculous: for it was really the work of Providence, as to me, that should order or appoint that ten of twelve grains of corn should remain unspoiled, when the rats had destroyed all the rest, as if it had been dropped from heaven; as also, that I should throw it out in that particular place, where, it being in the shade of a high rock, it sprang up immediately; whereas, if I had thrown it anywhere else, at that time, it would have been burned up and destroyed.

I carefully saved the ears of this corn, you may be sure, in their season, which was about the end of June; and laying up every corn, I resolved to sow them all again; hoping, in time, to have some quantity sufficient to supply me with bread. But it was not till the fourth year that I could allow myself the least grain of this corn to eat, and even then but sparingly, as I shall show afterwards in its order; for I lost all that I sowed the first season, by not observing the proper time; as I sowed just before the dry season, so that it never came up at all, at least not as it would have done: of which in its place.

Besides this barley, there were, as above, twenty or thirty stalks of rice, which I preserved with the same care; and whose use was of the same kind, or to the same purpose, viz., to make me bread, or rather food; for I found ways to cook it without baking, though I did that also after some time.—But to return to my Journal.

I worked excessively hard these three or four months, to get my wall done; and the 14th of April I closed it up; contriving to get into it, not by a door, but over the wall, by a ladder, that there might be no sign on the outside of my habitation.

April 16.—I finished the ladder; so I went up with the ladder to the top, and then pulled it up after me, and let it down in the inside; this was a complete enclosure to me; for within I had room enough, and nothing could come at me from without, unless it could first mount my wall.

The very next day after this wall was finished, I had almost all my labour overthrown at once, and myself killed; the case was thus:—As I was busy in the inside of it, behind my tent, just at the entrance into my cave, I was terribly frightened by a shock of an earthquake!

I was so much amazed with the thing itself (having never felt the like, nor discoursed with any one that had) that I was like one dead or stupefied; and the motion of the earth made my stomach sick, like one that was tossed at sea: but the noise of the falling of the rock awaked me, as it were; and rousing me from the stupefied condition I was in, filled me with horror, and I thought of nothing but the hill falling upon my tent and my household goods, and burying all at once; this sunk my very soul within me a second time.

After the third shock was over, and I felt no more for some time, I began to take courage; yet I had not heart enough to go over my wall again, for fear of being buried alive; but sat still upon the ground greatly cast down and disconsolate, not knowing what to do.

This set me thinking about what I had best do; concluding, that if the island was subject to earthquakes, there would be no living for me in a cave, but I must consider of building me some little hut in an open place, which I might surround with a wall, as I had done here, and so make myself secure from wild beasts or men; for if I stayed where I was, I should certainly, one time or other, be buried alive.

With these thoughts, I resolved to remove my tent from the place where it now stood, being just under the hanging precipice of the hill, and which, if it should be shaken again, would certainly fall upon my tent. I spent the next two days, being the 19th and 20th of April, in contriving where and how to remove my habitation. I resolved that I would go to work with all speed to build me a wall with piles and cables, etc., in a circle as before, and set my tent in it when it was finished; but that I would venture to stay where I was till it was ready, and fit to remove to. This was the 21st.

April 22.—The next morning I began to consider of means to put this measure into execution; and I was at a great loss about tools. I had three large axes, and abundance of hatchets (for we carried the hatchets for traffic with the Indians); but with much chopping and cutting knotty hard wood, they were all full of notches, and dull: and though I had a grindstone, I could not turn it and grind my tools. This caused me as much thought as a statesman would have bestowed upon a grand point of politics, or a judge upon the life and death of a man. At length I contrived a wheel with a string, to turn it with my foot, that I might have both my hands at liberty.

April 28, 29.—These two whole days I took up in grinding my tools, my machine for turning my grindstone performing very well.

April 30.—Having perceived that my bread had been low a great while, I took a survey of it, and reduced myself to one biscuit-cake a day, which made my heart very heavy.

SECTION IX

ROBINSON OBTAINS MORE ARTICLES FROM THE WRECK—ILLNESS AND AFFLICTION

MAY 1.—In the morning, looking towards the seaside, the tide being low, I saw something lie on the shore bigger than ordinary, and it looked like a cask; when I came to it I found a small barrel, and two or three pieces of the wreck of the ship, which were driven on shore by the late hurricane; and looking towards the wreck itself, I thought it seemed to lie higher out of the water than it used to do. I examined the barrel that was driven on shore, and soon found it was a barrel of gunpowder; but it had taken water, and the powder was caked as hard as a stone; however, I rolled it farther on the shore for the present, and went on upon the sands, as near as I could to the wreck of the ship, to look for more.

When I came down to the ship, I found it strangely removed. The forecastle, which lay buried in the sand was heaved up at least six feet; and the stern (which was broke to pieces, and parted from the rest, by the force of the sea, soon after I had left rummaging her) was tossed, as it were, up, and cast on one side: and the sand was thrown so high on that side next her stern, that I could now walk quite up to her when the tide was out.

This wholly diverted my thoughts from the design of removing my habitation; and I busied myself mightily, that day especially, in searching whether I could make any way into the ship; but I found nothing was to be expected of that kind, for all the inside of the ship was choked up with sand. However, as I had learned not to despair of anything, I resolved to pull everything to pieces that I could of the ship, concluding that everything I could get from her would be of some use or other to me.

May 3.—I began with my saw, and cut a piece of a beam through which I thought held some of the upper part or quarter-deck together; and when I had cut it through, I cleared away the sand as well as I could from the side which lay highest; but the tide coming in, I was obliged to give over for that time.

May 4.—I went a fishing, but caught not one fish that I durst eat of, till I was weary of my sport; when just going to leave off, I caught a young dolphin. I had made a long line of some rope-yarn, but I had no hooks; yet I frequently caught fish enough, as much as I cared to eat; all of which I dried in the sun, and ate them dry.

May 5 to 24.—Every day, to this day, I worked on the wreck; and with hard labour I loosened some things so much, with the crow, that the first blowing tide several casks floated out, and two of the seamen's chests; but the wind blowing from shore nothing came to the land that day but pieces of timber, and a hogshead, which had some Brazil pork in it. I continued this work every day to the 15th of June, except the time necessary to get food; which I always appointed, during this part of my employment, to be when the tide was up, that I might be ready when it was ebbed out; and by this time I had gotten timber, and plank, and iron work enough to have built a good boat if I had known how; and I also got, at several times, and in several pieces, near one hundred weight of the sheet-lead.

June 16.—Going down to the seaside, I found a large tortoise, or turtle. This was the first I had seen; which, it seems, was only to my misfortune, not any defect of the place or scarcity; for had I happened to be on the other side of the island, I might have had hundreds of them every day, as I found afterwards; but perhaps had paid dear enough for them.

June 17 I spent in cooking the turtle. I found in her

three score eggs; and her flesh was to me, at that time, the most savoury and pleasant that I ever tasted in my life; having no flesh, but of goats and fowls, since I landed in this horrid place.

June 18.—Rained all day, and I stayed within. I thought at this time, the rain felt cold, and I was somewhat chilly; which I knew was not usual in that latitude.

June 19.—Very ill, and shivering, as if the weather had been cold.

June 20.—No rest all night; violent pains in my head, and feverish.

June 21.—Very ill; frightened almost to death with the apprehensions of my sad condition, to be sick and no help; prayed to God, for the first time since the storm off Hull; but scarce knew what I said, or why, my thoughts being all confused.

June 22.—A little better; but under dreadful apprehensions of sickness.

June 23.—Very bad again; cold and shivering, and then a violent headache.

June 24.—Much better.

June 25.—An ague very violent; the fit held me seven hours; cold fit, and hot, with faint sweats after it.

June 26.—Better; and having no victuals to eat took my gun, but found myself very weak; however, I killed a she-goat, and with much difficulty got it home, and broiled some of it, and ate. I would fain have stewed it, and made some broth, but had no pot.

June 27.—The ague again so violently that I lay a-bed all day, and neither ate nor drank. I was ready to perish for thirst; but so weak, I had not the strength to stand up, or get myself any water to drink. Prayed to God again, but was light-headed; and when I was not, I was so ignorant that I knew not what to say; only lay and cried, "Lord, look upon me! Lord, pity me! Lord, have mercy upon me!" I suppose I did nothing else for two or three hours; till the fit wearing off, I fell asleep, and did not wake till far in the night.

When I awoke, I found myself much refreshed, but weak, and exceeding thirsty; however, as I had no water in my whole habitation, I was forced to lie till morning.

I had, alas! no divine knowledge: what I had received

by the good instruction of my father was then worn out, by an uninterrupted series, for eight years, of seafaring wickedness and a constant conversation with none but such as were, like myself, wicked and profane to the last degree.

But now, when I began to be sick, and a leisure view of the miseries of death came to place itself before me; when my spirits began to sink under the burden of a strong distemper, and nature was exhausted with the violence of the fever; conscience, that had slept so long, began to wake; and I reproached myself with my past life, in which I had so evidently, by uncommon wickedness provoked the justice of God to lay me under uncommon strokes, and to deal with me in so vindictive a manner.

"Now," said I, aloud, "my dead father's words are come to pass; God's justice has overtaken me, and I have none to help or hear me. Then I cried out, "Lord, be my help, for I am in great distress." This was the first prayer, if I may call it so, that I had made for many years. But I return to my Journal.

SECTION X

HIS RECOVERY—HIS COMFORT IN READING THE SCRIPTURES—MAKES AN EXCURSION INTO THE INTERIOR OF THE ISLAND—FORMS HIS "BOWER"

JUNE 28.—Having been somewhat refreshed with the sleep I had had, and the fit being entirely off, I got up, and considered now was my time to get something to refresh and support myself when I should be ill. The first thing I did was to fill a large case-bottle with water, and set it upon my table, in reach of my bed; and to take off the chill or aguish disposition of the water, I put about a quarter of a pint of rum into it, and mixed them together. Then I got a piece of the goat's flesh, and broiled it on the coals, but could eat very little. I walked about, but was very weak, and withal very sad and heavy-hearted in the sense of my miserable condition, dreading the return of my distemper the next day.

Now, as the apprehension of the return of my distemper

terrified me very much, it occurred to my thought, that the Brazilians take no physic but their tobacco for almost all distempers; and I had a piece of a roll of tobacco in one of the chests, which was cured; and some also that was green, and not quite cured.

I went, directed by Heaven, no doubt: for in this chest I found a cure both for soul and body. I opened the chest, and found what I looked for, viz., the tobacco; and as the few books I had saved lay there too, I took out one of the Bibles which I mentioned before, and which, to this time, I had not found leisure or so much as inclination, to look into. I say, I took it out, and brought both that and the tobacco with me to the table. What use to make of the tobacco I knew not, as to my distemper, nor whether it was good for it or not; but I tried several experiments with it, as if I was resolved it should hit one way or other. I first took a piece of a leaf, and chewed it in my mouth; which, indeed, at first, almost stupefied my brain; the tobacco being green and strong and such as I had not been much used to. Then I took some and steeped it an hour or two in some rum, and resolved to take a dose of it when I lay down; and lastly, I burnt some upon a pan of coals, and held my nose close over the smoke of it as long as I could bear it; as well for the heat, as almost for suffocation. In the interval of this operation, I took up the Bible, and began to read: but my head was too much disturbed by the tobacco to bear reading, at least at that time; only, having opened the book casually, the first words that occurred to me were these, "Call upon Me in the day of trouble, and I will deliver thee and thou shalt glorify Me."

It now grew late: and the tobacco had, as I said, dozed my head so much, that I inclined to sleep: so I left my lamp burning in the cave, lest I should want anything in the night, and went to bed. But before I lay down, I did what I had never done in all my life: I kneeled down, and prayed to God to fulfil the promise to me, that if I called upon Him in the day of trouble, He would deliver me. After my broken and imperfect prayer was over, I drank the rum in which I had steeped the tobacco; which was so strong and rank of the tobacco, that indeed I could scarce get it down; immediately upon this I went to bed. I found presently the rum flew up into my head violently; but I fell into a sound sleep, and waked no more till by the sun, it must necessarily be near three o'clock in the afternoon the next day. When I got up I was stronger than I was the day before, and my stomach better, for I was hungry; and, in short, I had no fit the next day, but continued much altered for the better. This was the 29th.

The 30th was my well day, of course; and I went abroad with my gun, but did not care to travel too far. I killed a seafowl or two, something like a brand goose, and brought them home; but was not very forward to eat them; so I ate some more of the turtle's eggs, which were very good. This evening I renewed the medicine, which I had supposed did me good the day before, viz., the tobacco steeped in rum; only I did not take so much as before, nor did I chew any of the leaf, or hold my head over the smoke: however, I was not so well the next day, which was the 1st of July, as I hoped I should have been; for I had a little of the cold fit, but it was not much.

July 2 and 3.—I renewed the medicine all the three ways; and dosed myself with it at first, and doubled the quantity which I drank.

July 4.—In the morning I took the Bible; and beginning at the New Testament, I began seriously to read it; and imposed upon myself to read a while every morning and every night; not binding myself to the number of chapters, but as long as my thoughts should engage me. It was not long after I set seriously to this work, that I found my heart sincerely affected with the wickedness of my past life. The words, "All these things have not brought thee to repentance," ran seriously in my thoughts. I was earnestly begging of God to give me repentance, when it happened providentially, the very same day, that reading the scripture I came to these words, "He is exalted a Prince and a Saviour; to give repentance, and to give remission." I threw down the book; and with my heart as well as my hands lifted up to heaven, in a kind of ecstasy of joy, I cried out aloud, "Jesus, thou son of David! Jesus, thou exalted Prince and Saviour! give me repentance." This was the first time in all my life I could say, in the true sense of the words, that I prayed; for now I prayed with a sense of my condition, and with a true scripture view of hope, founded on the encouragement of the word of God: and from this time, I may say I began to have hope that God would hear me.

It was on the 15th of July that I began to take a more particular survey of the island itself. I went up the creek first, where, as I hinted, I brought my rafts on shore. I found, after I came about two miles up, that the tide did not flow any higher; and that it was no more than a little brook of running water, very fresh and good: but this being the dry season, there was hardly any water in some parts of it; at least, not any stream. On the banks of this brook I found many pleasant savannahs or meadows, plain, smooth, and covered with grass; and on the rising parts of them, next to the higher grounds (where the water, as it might be supposed, never overflowed), I found a great deal of tobacco, green, and growing to a very great and strong stalk: and there were divers other plants, which I had no knowledge of, or understanding about, and that might, perhaps, have virtues of their own, which I could not find out. I saw several sugar-canes, but wild; and, for want of cultivation, imperfect.

The next day, the 16th, I went up the same way again; and after going something farther than I had gone the day before, I found the brook and the savannahs begin to cease, and the country become more woody than before. In this part I found different fruits; and particularly I found melons upon the ground in great abundance, and grapes upon the trees: the vines, indeed, had spread over the trees, and the clusters of grapes were now just in their prime, very ripe and rich. This was a surprising discovery and I was exceedingly glad of them, but I was warned by my experience to eat sparingly of them; remembering that when I was ashore in Barbary, the eating of grapes killed several of our Englishmen, who were slaves there, by throwing them into fluxes and fevers. I found, however, an excellent use for these grapes; and that was to cure or dry them in the sun, and keep them as dried grapes or raisins are kept; which I thought would be (as indeed they were) as wholesome and as agreeable to eat, when no grapes were to be had.

Having spent three days in this journey, I came home, so I must now call my tent and my cave.

When I came home from this journey, I contemplated

with great pleasure the fruitfulness of that valley, and the pleasantness of the situation; the security from storms on that side; the water and the wood; and concluded that I had pitched upon a place to fix my abode in, which was by far the worst part of the country. Upon the whole, I began to consider of removing my habitation, and to look out for a place equally safe as where I was now situate; if possible, in that pleasant fruitful part of the island.

I was so enamoured of this place, that I spent much of my time there for the whole remaining part of the month of July; and though, upon second thoughts, I resolved not to remove, yet I built me a little kind of a bower, and surrounded it at a distance with a strong fence, being a double hedge, as high as I could reach, well staked, and filled between with brushwood. Here I lay very secure sometimes two or three nights together; always going over it with a ladder, as before: so that I fancied now I had my country and my seacoast house. This work took me up to the beginning of August.

About the beginning of August, I had finished my bower, and began to enjoy myself. The 3rd of August, I found the grapes I had hung up were perfectly dried, and indeed were excellent good raisins of the sun; so I began to take them down from the trees; and it was very happy that I did so, as the rains which followed would have spoiled them, and I should have lost the best part of my winter food; for I had above two hundred large bunches of them. No sooner had I taken them all down, and carried most of them home to my cave, but it began to rain: and from hence, which was the 14th of August, it rained, more or less, every day till the middle of October; and sometimes so violently, that I could not stir out of my cave for several days.

In this season, I was much surprised with the increase of my family. I had been concerned for the loss of one of my cats, who ran away from me, or, as I thought, had been dead; and I heard no more of her, till, to my astonishment, she came home with three kittens. This was the more strange to me, because, about the end of August, though I had killed a wild cat, as I called it, with my gun, yet I thought it was quite a different kind from our European cats: yet the young cats were the same kind of house-breed as the old one; and both of my cats being females, I thought it very strange. But from these three I afterwards came to be so pestered with cats that I was forced to kill them like vermin, or wild beasts, and to drive them from my house as much as possible.

From the 14th of August to the 26th, incessant rain; so that I could not stir, and was now very careful not to be much wet. In this confinement, I began to be straitened for food, but venturing out twice, I one day killed a goat, and the last day, which was the 24th, found a very large tortoise, which was a treat to me. My food was now regulated thus: I ate a bunch of raisins for my breakfast; a piece of the goat's flesh, or of the turtle, broiled for my dinner (for, to my great misfortune, I had no vessel to boil or stew anything), and two or three of the turtle's eggs for my supper.

During this confinement in my cover from the rain, I worked daily two or three hours at enlarging my cave; and by degrees worked it on towards one side, till I came to the outside of the hill: and made a door, or way out, which came beyond my fence or wall, and so I came in and out this way. But I was not perfectly easy at lying so open, for as I had managed myself before, I was in a perfect enclosure; whereas now, I thought I lay exposed; and yet I could not perceive that there was any living thing to fear, the biggest creature that I had as yet seen upon the island being a goat.

September 30.—I was now come to the unhappy anniversary of my landing: I cast up the notches on my post, and found I had been on shore three hundred and sixty-five days. I kept this day as a solemn fast! setting it apart for religious exercise, prostrating myself on the ground with the most serious humiliation, confessing my sins to God, acknowledging His righteous judgments upon me, and praying to Him to have mercy on me through Jesus Christ; and having not tasted the least refreshment for twelve hours, even till the going down of the sun, I then ate a biscuit and a bunch of grapes, and went to bed, finishing the day as I began it. I had all this time observed no sabbath day; for as at first I had no sense of religion upon my mind, I had, after some time, omitted to distinguish the weeks, by making a longer notch than ordinary for the sabbath-day, and so did not really know what any of the days were: but now having cast up the days, as above, I found I had been there a year; so I divided it into weeks, and set apart every seventh day for a sabbath: though I found, at the end of my account, I had lost a day or two in my reckoning. A little after this, my ink beginning to fail me, I contented myself to use it more sparingly; and to write down only the most remarkable events of my life.

The rainy season and the dry season began now to appear regular to me, and I learned to divide them so as to provide for them accordingly; but I bought all my experience before I had it.

While my corn was growing, I made a little discovery, which was of use to me afterwards. As soon as the rains were over, and the weather began to settle, which was about the month of November, I made a visit up the country to my bower; where, though I had not been for some months, yet I found all things just as I had left them. The circle or double hedge that I had made was not only firm and entire, but the stakes which I had cut out of some trees that grew thereabouts, were all shot out and grown with long branches as much as a willow tree usually shoots the first year after lopping its head; but I could not tell what tree to call it that these stakes were cut from. I was surprised, and yet very well pleased, to see the young trees grow; and I pruned them, and led them to grow as much alike as I could: and it is scarce credible how beautiful a figure they grew into in three years: so that, though the hedge made a circle of about twenty-five yards in diameter, yet the trees, for such I might call them, soon covered it, and it was a complete shade, sufficient to lodge under all the dry season. This made me resolve to cut some more stakes, and make me a hedge like this, in a semicircle round my wall (I mean that of my first dwelling), which I did: and placing the trees or stakes in a double row, at about eight yards distance from my fence, they grew presently; and were at first a fine cover to my habitation, and afterwards served for a defence also; as I shall observe in its order.

SECTION XI

ROBINSON MAKES A TOUR TO EXPLORE HIS ISLAND

I FOUND now that the seasons of the year might generally be divided, not into summer and winter as in Europe, but into the rainy seasons and the dry seasons, which were generally thus: From the middle of February to the middle of April, rainy; the sun being then on or near the equinox. From the middle of April till the middle of August, dry; the sun being then north of the Line. From the middle of August till the middle of October, rainy; the sun being then come back to the Line. From the middle of October till the middle of February, dry; the sun being then to the south of the Line.

The rainy seasons held sometimes longer and sometimes shorter, as the winds happened to blow; but this was a general observation I made. After I had found, by experience, the ill consequences of being abroad in the rain, I took care to furnish myself with provisions beforehand, that I might not be obliged to go out; and I sat within doors as much as possible during the wet months. In this time I found much employment, and very suitable also to the time; as I found great occasion for many things which I had no way to furnish myself with, but by hard labour and constant application; particularly, I tried many ways to make myself a basket; but all the twigs I could get for the purpose proved so brittle that they would do nothing. It proved of excellent advantage to me now, that when I was a boy, I used to take great delight in standing at a basket-maker's in the town where my father lived, to see them make their wicker-ware; and being, as boys usually are, very officious to help, and a great observer of the manner how they worked these things, and sometimes lending a hand, I had by these means full knowledge of the methods of it, so that I wanted nothing but the materials; when it came into my mind, that the twigs of that tree from whence I cut my stakes that grew, might possibly be as tough as the sallows, willows, and osiers, in England, and I resolved to try. Accordingly, the next day, I went to my country house, as I called it, and cutting some of the smaller twigs, I found them to my purpose as much as

I could desire; whereupon I came the next time prepared with a hatchet to cut down a quantity, which I soon found, for there was great plenty of them. These I set up to dry within my circle or hedge; and when they were fit for use, I carried them to my cave; and there, during the next season I employed myself in making, as well as I could, several baskets; both to carry earth, or carry or lay up anything I had occasion for. Though I did not finish them very handsomely, yet I made them sufficiently serviceable for my purpose; and thus, afterwards, I took care never to be without them; and as my wicker-ware decayed, I made more; especially strong deep baskets to place my corn in, instead of sacks, when I should come to have any quantity of it.

I mentioned before, that I had great mind to see the whole island; and that I had travelled up the brook, and so on to where I had built my bower, and where I had an opening quite to the sea, on the other side of the island. I now resolved to travel quite across to the seashore, on that side; so taking my gun, a hatchet, and my dog, and a larger quantity of powder and shot than usual, with two biscuit-cakes, and a great bunch of raisins in my pouch, for my store, I began my journey. When I had passed the vale where my bower stood, as above, I came within view of the sea, to the west; and it being a clear day, I fairly descried land, whether an island or continent I could not tell; but it lay very high, extending from W. to W.S.W. at a very great distance; by my guess, it could not be less than fifteen or twenty leagues off.

I could not tell what part of the world this might be; otherwise than that I knew it must be part of America, and as I concluded by all my observations, must be near the Spanish dominions; and perhaps was all inhabited by savages, where, if I should have landed, I had been in a worse condition than I was now. I considered that if this land was the Spanish coast, I should certainly one time or other, see some vessel pass or repass one way or other; but if not, then it was a savage coast between the Spanish country and the Brazils, whose inhabitants are indeed the worst savages; for they are cannibals, or men-eaters, and fail not to murder and devour all human beings that fall into their hands.

With these considerations, walking very leisurely forward,

I found this side of the island, where I now was, much pleasanter than mine; the open or savannah field sweetly adorned with flowers and grass, and full of very fine woods. I saw abundance of parrots; and fain would have caught one, if possible, to have kept it to be tame, and taught it to speak to me. I did after taking some pains, catch a young parrot; for I knocked it down with a stick, and, having recovered it, I brought it home; but it was years before I could make him speak; however, at last I taught him to call me by my name very familiarly.

I was exceedingly amused with this journey. I found in the low grounds hares, as I thought them to be, and foxes; but they differed greatly from all the other kinds I had met with; nor could I satisfy myself to eat them, though I killed several. But I had no need to be venturous, for I had no want of food, and of that which was very good too; especially these three sorts, viz., goats, pigeons, and turtle, or tortoise.

As soon as I came to the seashore, I was surprised to see that I had taken up my lot on the worst side of the island; for here indeed the shore was covered with innumerable turtles; whereas, on the other side I had found but three in a year and a half. Here was also an infinite number of fowls of many kinds; some of which I had not seen before, and many of them very good meat, but such as I knew not the names of, except those called penguins.

I confess this side of the country was much pleasanter than mine; yet I had not the least inclination to remove; for as I was fixed in my habitation, it became natural to me, and I seemed all the while I was here to be as it were upon a journey, and from home. However, I travelled along the seashore towards the east, I suppose about twelve miles, and then setting up a great pole upon the seashore for a mark, I concluded I would go home again; and that the next journey I took should be on the other side of the island, east from my dwelling, and so round till I came to my post again; of which in its place.

I took another way to come back than that I went, thinking I could easily keep so much of the island in my view, that I could not miss finding my first dwelling by viewing the country; but I found myself mistaken; for being come about two or three miles, I found myself descended in a very large valley, but so surrounded with hills, and those hills covered with wood, that I could not see which was my way by any direction but that of the sun, nor even then, unless I knew very well the position of the sun at that time of the day. And it happened to my farther misfortune, that the weather proved hazy for three or four days while I was in this valley; and not being able to see the sun, I wandered about very uncomfortable, and at last was obliged to find out the seaside, look for my post, and come back the same way I went; and then by easy journeys I turned homeward, the weather being exceeding hot, and my gun, ammunition, hatchet, and other things very heavy.

SECTION XII

HE RETURNS TO HIS CAVE—HIS AGRICULTURAL LABOURS AND SUCCESS

In this journey, my dog surprised a young kid and seized upon it; and I, running to take hold of it, caught it and saved it alive from the dog. I had a great mind to bring it home if I could; for I had often been musing whether it might not be possible to get a kid or two, and so raise a breed of tame goats, which might supply me with food when my powder and shot were all spent. I made a collar for this little creature, and with a string which I had made of some rope yarn, which I always carried about me, I led him along, though with some difficulty, till I came to my bower, and there I enclosed him and left him; for I was very impatient to be at home, from whence I had been absent above a month.

I reposed myself here a week, to rest and regale myself after my long journey; during which, most of the time was taken up in the weighty affair of making a cage for my Poll, who began now to be more domestic, and to be mighty well acquainted with me Then I began to think of the poor kid which I had penned within my little circle, and resolved to fetch it home, or give it some food; accordingly I went, and found it where I left it (for indeed it could not get out), but was almost starved for want of food. I went and cut boughs of trees, and branches of such shrubs as I could find, and having fed it, I tied it as I did before, to lead it away; but it was so tame with being hungry, that I had no need to have tied it, for it followed me like a dog; and as I continually fed it, the creature became so loving, so gentle, and so fond, that it was from that time one of my domestics also, and would never leave me afterwards.

Thus, I began my third year; and though I have not given the reader the trouble of so particular an account of my works this year as the first, yet in general it may be observed, that I was very seldom idle, having regularly divided my time, according to the several daily employments that were before me; such as, first, My duty to God, and reading the scriptures, which I constantly set apart some time for, thrice every day: secondly, Going abroad with my gun for food, which generally took me up three hours every morning, when it did not rain: thirdly, The ordering, curing, preserving, and cooking what I had killed or catched for my supply; these took up great part of the day, when the sun was in the zenith the violence of the heat was too great to stir out; so that about four hours in the evening was all the time I could be supposed to work in; with this exception, that sometimes I changed my hours of hunting and working, and went to work in the morning, and abroad with my gun in the afternoon.

To this short time allowed for labour, I desire may be added the exceeding laboriousness of my work; the many hours which, for want of tools, want of help, and want of skill, everything I did took up out of my time; for example, I was full two and forty days making me a board for a long shelf, which I wanted in my cave; whereas, two sawyers, with their tools and a sawpit, would cut six of them out of the same tree in half a day.

My case was this; it was a large tree that was to be cut down, because my board was to be a broad one. This tree I was three days cutting down, and two more in cutting off the boughs, and reducing it to a log, or piece of timber. With inexpressible hacking and hewing, I reduced both sides of it into chips, till it was light enough to move; then I turned it, and made one side of it smooth and flat as a board, from end to end; then turning that side downward, cut the other side, till I brought the plank to be about three inches thick, and smooth on both sides. Any one may judge the labour of my hands in such a piece of work; but labour and patience carried me through that, and many other things; I only observe this in particular, to show the reason why so much of my time went away with so little work, viz., that what might be a little to be done with help and tools was a vast labour, and required a prodigious time to do alone, and by hand. Notwithstanding this, with patience and labour I went through many things; and, indeed, everything that my circumstances made necessary for me to do, as will appear by what follows.

I was now, in the months of November and December, expecting my crop of barley and rice. The ground I had manured or dug up for them was not great; for, as I observed, my seed of each was not more than half a peck, having lost one whole crop by sowing in the dry season: but now my crop promised very well; when, on a sudden I found I was in danger of losing it again by enemies of several sorts, which it was scarce possible to keep from it; as, first, the goats and wild creatures which I called hares, who, tasting the sweetness of the blade, lay in it night and day, as soon as it came up, and ate it so close, that it could get no time to shoot up into stalk.

I saw no remedy for this, but by making an enclosure about it with a hedge, which I did with a great deal of toil; and the more, because it required speed. However, as my arable land was but small, suited to my crop, I got it tolerably well fenced in about three weeks' time; and shooting some of the creatures in the daytime, I set my dog to guard it at night, tying him up to a stake at the gate, where he would stand and bark all night long; so in a little time the enemies forsook the place, and the corn grew very strong and well, and began to ripen apace.

But as the beasts ruined me before, while my corn was in the blade, so the birds were likely to ruin me now, when it was in the ear; for going along by the place to see how it throve, I saw my little crop surrounded with fowls, I knew not of how many sorts, who stood as it were, watching till I should be gone. I immediately let fly among them, for I always had my gun with me, and killed three of them. I took them up, and served them as we serve notorious thieves in England, viz., hanged them in chains, for a terror to others. It is impossible to imagine that this should have such an effect as it had; for the fowls not only never came to the corn, but, in short, they forsook all that part of the island, and I could never see a bird near the place as long as my scarecrows hung there. This I was very glad of, you may be sure; and about the latter end of December, which was our second harvest of the year, I reaped my corn.

I was sadly put to it for a scythe or sickle to cut it down: and all I could do was to make one as well as I could, out of one of the broad swords or cutlasses, which I saved among the arms of the ship. However, as my first crop was but small, I had no difficulty to cut it down: in short, I reaped it my way, for I cut nothing off but the ears, and carried it away in a great basket which I had made, and so rubbed it out with my hands; and at the end of all my harvesting, I found that out of my half peck of seed I had near two bushels of rice, and above two bushels and a half of barley; that is to say, by my guess, for I had no measure.

However, this was great encouragement to me; and I foresaw that, in time, it would please God to supply me with bread; yet here I was perplexed again; for I neither knew how to grind or make meal of my corn, or indeed how to clean it and part it; nor if made into meal, how to make bread of it; and if how to make it, yet I knew not how to bake it; these things being added to my desire of having a good quantity for store, and to secure a constant supply, I resolved not to taste any of this crop, but to preserve it all for seed against the next season; and, in the meantime, to employ all my study and hours of working to accomplish this great work of providing myself with corn and bread.

It might be truly said, that now I worked for my bread. It is a little wonderful, and what I believe few people have thought much upon, viz., the strange multitude of little things necessary in the providing, producing, curing, dressing, making, and finishing this one article of bread. I that was reduced to a mere state of nature, found this to my daily discouragement and was made more sensible of it every hour, even after I had got the first handful of seed corn, which, as I have said, came up unexpectedly, and indeed, as a surprise.

First, I had no plough to turn up the earth; no spade or shovel to dig it; well, this I conquered by making a wooden spade, as I observed before; but this did my work in but a wooden manner. The corn was sown; I had no harrow, but was forced to go over it myself, and drag a great heavy bough of a tree over it, to scratch it, as it may be called, rather than rake or harrow it. Then I wanted a mill to grind it, sieves to dress it; yeast and salt to make it into bread, and an oven to bake it; and yet all these things I did without, as shall be observed; and the corn was an inestimable comfort and advantage to me; and as I resolved to use none of the corn for bread till I had a greater quantity by me, I had the next six months to apply myself wholly, by labour and invention, to furnish myself with utensils proper for the performing all the operations necessary for making corn fit for my use.

SECTION XIII

HIS MANUFACTURE OF POTTERY, AND CONTRIVANCE FOR BAKING BREAD

But now I was to prepare more land; for I had seed enough to sow above an acre of ground. Before I did this I had a week's work at least to make me a spade; which, when it was done, was but a sorry one indeed, and very heavy and required double labour to work with it; however, I went through that, and sowed my seed in two large flat pieces of ground, as near my house as I could find them to my mind, and fenced them in with a good hedge; the stakes of which were all cut off that wood which I had set before, and knew it would grow; so that, in one year's time, I knew I should have a quick or living hedge, that would want but little repair. This work took me up full three months; because a great part of the time was in the wet season, when I could not go abroad. Within doors, that is, when it rained, and I could not go out, I found employment on the following occasions; always observing that while I was at work, I diverted myself with talking to my parrot, and teaching him to speak; and I quickly taught him to know his own name, and at last to speak it out pretty loud, Poll; which was the first word I ever heard spoken in the island by any mouth but my own. This, therefore, was not my work, but an assistant to my work; for now, as I said, I had a great employment upon my hands, as follows: I had long studied, by some means or other, to make myself some earthen vessels, which indeed I wanted much, but knew not where to come at them; however, considering the heat of the climate, I did not doubt but if I could find out any clay, I might botch up some such pot as might, being dried in the sun, be hard and strong enough to bear handling, and to hold anything that was dry, and required to be kept so; and as this was necessary in preparing corn, meal, etc., which was the thing I was upon, I resolved to make some as large as I could, and fit only to stand like jars, to hold what should be put into them.

It would make the reader pity me, or rather laugh at me, to tell how many awkward ways I took to raise this paste; what odd misshapen ugly things I made; how many of them fell in, and how many fell out, the clay not being stiff enough to bear its own weight; how many cracked by the over violent heat of the sun, being set out too hastily; and how many fell in pieces with only removing, as well before as after they were dried; and, in a word, how, after having laboured hard to find the clay to dig it, to temper it, to bring it home, and work it, I could not make above two large earthen ugly things (I cannot call them jars) in about two months' labour.

However, as the sun baked these two very dry and hard, I lifted them very gently up, and set them down again in two great wicker baskets, which I had made on purpose for them, that they might not break; and as between the pot and the basket there was a little room to spare, I stuffed it full of the rice and barley straw; and these two pots being to stand always dry, I thought would hold my dry corn, and perhaps the meal, when the corn was bruised.

Though I miscarried so much in my design for large pots, yet I made several smaller things with better success; such as little round pots, flat dishes, pitchers, and pipkins, and everything my hand turned to; and the heat of the sun baked them very hard.

But all this would not answer my end, which was to get an earthen pot to hold liquids, and bear the fire, which none of these could do. It happened some time after, making a pretty large fire for cooking my meat, when I went to put it out after I had done with it, I found a broken piece of one of my earthenware vessels in the fire, burnt as hard as a stone, and red as a tile. I was agreeably surprised to see it; and said to myself that certainly they might be made to burn whole, if they would burn broken.

This set me to study how to order my fire, so as to make it burn some pots. I had no notion of a kiln, such as the potters burn in, or of glazing them with lead, though I had some lead to do it with; but I placed three pipkins and two or three pots in a pile, one upon another, and placed my firewood all round it, with a great heap of embers under them. I plied the fire with fresh fuel round the outside, and upon the top, till I saw pots in the inside red-hot quite through, and observed that they did not crack at all; when I saw them clear red, I let them stand in that heat about five or six hours, till I found one of them, though it did not crack, did melt or run; for the sand which was mixed with the clay melted by the violence of the heat, and would have run into glass, if I had gone on, so I slacked my fire gradually, till the pots began to abate of the red colour; and watching them all night, that I might not let the fire abate too fast, in the morning I had three very good, I will not say handsome, pipkins, and two other earthen pots, as hard burnt as could be desired; and one of them perfectly glazed with the running of the sand.

My next concern was to get a stone mortar to beat some corn in; for as to the mill, there was no thought of arriving to that perfection of art with one pair of hands. To supply this want I was at a great loss; for, of all trades in the world, I was as perfectly unqualified for a stone-cutter as for any whatever; neither had I any tools to go about it with. I spent a day to find out a great stone big enough to cut hollow, and made fit for a mortar; but could find none at all, except what was in the solid rock and which I had no way to dig or cut out; nor, indeed, were the rocks in the island of sufficient hardness, as they were all of a sandy, crumbling stone which would neither bear the weight of a heavy pestle, nor, would break the corn without filling it with sand; so, after a great deal of time lost in looking for a stone, I gave it over, and resolved to look for a block of hard wood, which I found indeed much easier; and getting one as big as I had strength to stir, I rounded and formed it on the outside with my axe and hatchet; and then with the help of the fire and infinite labour, made a hollow in it, as the Indians in Brazil make their canoes. After this, I made a great heavy pestle, or beater, of the wood called iron-wood; and this I prepared and laid by against I had my next crop of corn, when I proposed to myself to grind, or rather pound, my corn into meal, to make my bread.

The baking part was the next thing to be considered, and how I should make bread when I came to have corn; for first, I had no yeast; as to that part, there was no supplying the want, so I did not concern myself much about it; but for an oven I was indeed puzzled. At length I found out an expedient for that also, which was this: I made some earthen vessels very broad, but not deep, that is to say, about two feet diameter, and not above nine inches deep; these I burned in the fire, as I had done the other, and laid them by; and when I wanted to bake, I made a great fire upon my hearth, which I had paved with some square tiles, of my own making and burning also; but I should not call them square. When the firewood was burnt to embers, or live coals, I drew them forward upon the heart, so as to cover it all over, and there let them lie till the hearth was very hot; then sweeping away all the embers, I set down my loaf or loaves, and covering them with the earthen pot, drew the embers all round the outside of the pot, to keep in and add to the heat; and thus, as well as in the best oven in the world, I baked my barley loaves, and became in a little time, a good pastrycook into the bargain; for I made myself several cakes and puddings of the rice; but made no pies, as I had nothing to put into them except the flesh of fowls or goats.

And now, indeed, my stock of corn increasing, I really wanted to build my barns bigger; I wanted a place to lay it up in; for the increase of the corn now yielded me so much, that I had of the barley about twenty bushels, and of rice as much, or more, insomuch that now I resolved to begin to use it freely; for my bread had been quite gone a great while; I resolved also to see what quantity would be sufficient for me a whole year, and to sow but once a year.

Upon the whole, I found that the forty bushels of barley and rice were much more than I could consume in a year; so I resolved to sow just the same quantity every year that I sowed the last, in hopes that such a quantity would fully provide me with bread, etc.

SECTION XIV

MEDITATES HIS ESCAPE FROM THE ISLAND—BUILDS A CANOE—FAILURE OF HIS SCHEME—RESIGNATION TO HIS CONDITION—MAKES HIMSELF A NEW DRESS

ALL the while these things were doing, you may be sure my thoughts ran many times upon the prospect of land which I had seen from the other side of the island; and I was not without some secret wishes that I was on shore there; fancying, that seeing the main land, and an inhabited country, I might find some way or other to convey myself farther, and perhaps at last find some means of escape.

Now I wished for my boy Xury, and the long-boat with the shoulder-of-mutton sail, with which I sailed above a thousand miles on the coast of Africa; but this was in vain; then I thought I would go and look at our ship's boat, which, as I have said, was blown up upon the shore a great way, in the storm, when we were first cast away. She lay nearly where she did at first, but not quite, having turned by the force of the waves and the winds, almost bottom upward, against a high ridge of beachy rough sand; but no water about her as before. If I had had hands to have refitted her, and to have launched her into the water, the boat would have done very well, and I might have gone back into the Brazils with her easily enough; but I might have foreseen that I could no more turn her and set her upright upon her bottom, than I could remove the island; however, I went to the woods, and cut levers and rollers, and brought them to the boat, resolving to try what I could do; suggesting to myself, that if I could but turn her down, and repair the damage she had received, she would be a very good boat, and I might venture to sea in her.

I spared no pain, indeed, in this piece of fruitless toil, and spent, I think, three or four weeks about it; at last, finding it impossible to heave her up with my little strength, I fell to digging away the sand, to undermine her, and so as to make her fall down, setting pieces of wood to thrust and guide her right in the fall. But when I had done this, I was unable to stir her up again, or to get under her, much less to move her forward toward the water; so I was forced to give it over; and yet, though I gave over the hopes of the boat, my desire to venture over the main increased, rather than diminished, as the means for it seemed impossible.

In the middle of this work, I finished my fourth year in this place, and kept my anniversary with the same devotion and with as much comfort as before; for, by a constant study and serious application to the word of God, and by the assistance of His grace, I gained a different knowledge from what I had before; I entertained different notion of things.

I spent whole hours, I may say whole days, in representing to myself, in the most lively colours, how I must have acted if I had got nothing out of the ship. I could not have so much as got any food, except fish and turtles; and that, as it was long before I found any of them, I must have perished, like a mere savage; that if I had killed a goat or a fowl, by any contrivance, I had no way to flay or open it, or part the flesh from the skin, and pull it to pieces with my claws, like a beast.

These reflections made me very sensible of the goodness of Providence to me, and very thankful for my present condition, with all its hardships and misfortunes; and this part also I cannot but recommend to the reflection of those who are apt, in their misery, to say, "Is any affliction like mine?" Let them consider how much worse the cases of some people are, and their case would have been, if Providence had thought fit.

My clothes now began to decay mightily; as to linen, I had none for a great while, except some chequered shirts which I found in the chests of the other seamen, and which I carefully preserved, because many times I could bear no clothes on but a shirt, and it was a very great help to me that I had, among all the men's clothes of the ship, almost three dozen of shirts.

I began to consider about putting the few rags I had, which I called clothes, into some order. I had worn out all the waistcoats I had, and my business was now to try if I could not make jackets out of the great watch-coats that I had by me, and with such other materials as I had; so I set to work a-tailoring, or rather, indeed, a-botching, for I made most piteous work of it. However, I made shift to make two or three new waistcoats, which I hoped would serve me a great while.

I have mentioned that I saved the skins of all the creatures that I killed, I mean four-footed ones, and I had hung them up, stretched out with sticks in the sun, by which means some of them were so dry and hard that they were fit for little, but others I found very useful. The first thing I made of these was a great cap for my head, with the hair on the outside, to shoot off the rain; and this I performed so well, that after this I made me a suit of clothes wholly of the skins, that is to say, a waistcoat, and breeches open at the knees, and both loose; for they were rather wanting to keep me cool than warm. I must not omit to acknowledge that they were wretchedly made; for if I was a bad carpenter, I was a worse tailor. However, they were such as I made very good shift with; and when I was abroad, if it happened to rain, the hair of my waistcoat and cap being uppermost, I was kept very dry.

After this, I spent a great deal of time and pains to make me an umbrella. I made one and covered it with skins, the hair upwards, so that it cast off the rain like a penthouse, and kept off the sun so effectually, that I could walk out in the hottest of the weather with greater advantage than I could before in the coolest; and when I had no need of it, could close it and carry it under my arm.

Thus I lived mightily comfortably, my mind being entirely composed by resigning to the will of God, and throwing myself wholly upon the disposal of His providence. This made my life better than sociable; for when I began to regret the want of conversation, I would ask myself, whether thus conversing mutually with my own thoughts, and as I hope I may say with even God Himself, by ejaculations, was not better than the utmost enjoyment of human society in the world?

SECTION XV

HE MAKES A SMALLER CANOE, IN WHICH HE ATTEMPTS TO CRUISE ROUND THE ISLAND—HIS PERILOUS SITUATION AT SEA—HE RETURNS HOME

I CANNOT say that after this, for five years, any extraordinary thing happened to me, but I lived on in the same course, in the same posture and place, just as before; the chief things I was employed in, besides my yearly labour of planting my barley and rice, and curing my raisins, of both which I always kept up just enough to have sufficient stock of one year's provision beforehand; I say, besides this yearly labour, and my daily pursuit of going out with my gun, I had one labour, to make a canoe, which at last I finished; so that by digging a canal to it six feet wide, and four feet deep, I brought it into the creek, almost half a mile.

However, though my little periagua was finished, yet the size of it was not at all answerable to the design which I had in view at first; I mean, of venturing over to the *terra firma*, where it was above forty miles broad; accordingly, the smallness of my boat assisted to put an end to that design, and now I thought no more of it. As I had my boat, my next design was to make a cruise around the island; for as I had been on the other side in one place, crossing, as I had already described over the land, so the discoveries I made in that little journey made me very eager to see other parts of the coast: and now I had a boat I thought of nothing but sailing round the island.

It was on the sixth of November, in the sixth year of my reign, or my captivity, which you please, that I set out in this voyage, and I found it much longer than I expected; for though the island itself was not very large, yet when I came to the east side of it, I found a great ledge of rocks lie out about two leagues into the sea, some above water, some under it; and beyond that a shoal of sand, lying dry half a league more, so that I was obliged to go a great way out to sea to double the point.

When first I discovered them, I was going to give over my enterprise, and come back again, not knowing how far it might oblige me to go out to sea, and above all, doubting how I should get back again; so I came to an anchor with a piece of broken grappling which I got out of the ship.

Having secured my boat, I took my gun and went on shore, climbing up on a hill, which seemed to overlook that point, where I saw the full extent of it, and resolved to venture.

In my viewing the sea from that hill where I stood, I perceived a strong, and indeed a most furious current, which ran to the east, and even came close to the point; and I took the more notice of it, because I saw there might be some danger that when I came into it, I might be carried out to sea by the strength of it, and not be able to make the island again; and, indeed, had I not got first upon this hill, I believe it would have been so; for there was the same current on the other side of the island, only that it set off at a farther distance, and I saw there was a strong eddy under the shore; so I had nothing to do but to get out of the first current, and I should presently be in an eddy.

I lay here, however, two days, because the wind blowing pretty fresh at E.S.E., and that being just contrary to the said current, made a great breach of the sea upon the point; so that it was not safe for me to keep too close to the shore, for the breach, not to go too far off, because of the stream.

The third day, in the morning, the wind having abated overnight the sea was calm and I ventured; but I am a warning piece again to all rash and ignorant pilots; for no sooner was I come to the point, when I was not even my boat's length from the shore, but I found myself in a great depth of water, and a current like the sluice of a mill; it carried my boat along with it with such violence, that all I could do could not keep her so much as on the edge of it; but I found it hurried me farther and farther out from the eddy, which was on my left hand. There was no wind stirring to help me, and all I could do with my paddles signified nothing; and now I began to give myself over for lost, for as the current was on both sides of the island, I knew in a few leagues' distance they must join again, and then I was irrecoverably gone; nor did I see any possibility of avoiding it, so that I had no prospect before me but of perishing, not by the sea, for that was calm enough, but of starving for hunger. I had indeed found a tortoise on the shore, as big almost as I could lift, and had tossed it into the boat, and I had a great jar of fresh water, that is to say, one of my earthen pots; but what was all this to being driven into the vast ocean, where there was no shore, no main land or island, for a thousand leagues at least?

It is scarce possible to imagine the consternation I was now in, being driven from my beloved island (for so it appeared to me now to be) into the wide ocean, almost two leagues, and in the utmost despair, of ever recovering it again. However, I worked hard, till indeed my strength was almost exhausted, and kept my boat as much to the northward, that is, towards the side of the current which the eddy lay on, as possibly I could; when about noon, as the sun passed the meridian, I thought I felt a little breeze of wind in my face, springing up from S.S.E. This cheered my heart a little and especially when, in about half an hour more, it blew a pretty gentle gale. By this time I was got at a frightful distance from the island, and had the least cloudy or hazy weather intervened, I had been undone another way too; for I had no compass on board and should never have known how to have steered towards the island, if I had but once lost sight of it; but the weather continuing clear, I applied myself to get up my mast again, and spread my sail, standing away to the north as much as possible to get out of the current.

Just as I had set my mast and sail, and the boat began to stretch away I saw even by the clearness of the water some alteration of the current was near; for where the current was so strong, the water was foul; but perceiving the water clear, I found the current abate; and presently I found to the east at about half a mile, a breach of the sea upon some rocks; these rocks I found caused the current to part again, and as the main stress of it ran away more southerly, leaving the rocks to the north-east, so the other returned by the repulse of the rocks, and made a strong eddy which ran back again to the north-west, with a very sharp stream.

I put my boat into the stream of this eddy, and the wind also freshening how gladly I spread my sail to it, running cheerfully before the wind, and with a strong tide or eddy under foot.

About four o'clock in the evening, being then within a league of the island, I found the point of the rocks which occasioned this disaster stretching out, as is described before, to the southward, and casting off the current more southerly had, of course, made another eddy to the north; and this I found very strong, but not directly setting the way my course lay, which was due west, but almost full north. However, having a fresh gale, I stretched across this eddy, slanting north-west and in about an hour, came within about a mile of the shore, where, it being smooth water I soon got to land.

When I was on shore, I fell on my knees, and gave God thanks for my deliverance, resolving to lay aside all thoughts of my deliverance by my boat; and refreshing myself with such things as I had, I brought my boat close to the shore, in a little cove that I had spied under some trees, and laid me down to sleep, being quite spent with the labour and fatigue of the voyage.

I now had enough of rambling to sea for some time, and had enough to do for many days to sit still, and to reflect upon the danger I had been in. I should have been very glad to have had my boat again on my side of the island; but I knew not how it was practicable to get it round. So with these thoughts, I contented myself to be without any boat, though it had been the product of so many months' labour to make it, and of so many more to get it into the sea.

In this government of my temper I remained near a year, lived a very sedate, retired life as you may well suppose; and my thoughts being very much composed as to my condition, and fully comforted in resigning myself to the dispositions of Providence, I thought I lived really very happily in all things, except that of society.

I improved myself in this time in all the mechanic

exercises which my necessities put me upon applying myself to; and I believe I could, upon occasion, have made a very good carpenter, especially considering how few tools I had.

Besides this, I arrived at an unexpected perfection in my earthenware, and contrived well enough to make them with a wheel, which I found infinitely easier and better; because I made things round and shapeable which before were filthy things indeed to look upon. But I think I was never more vain of my performance, or more joyful for anything I found out than for my being able to make a tobacco-pipe: and though it was a very ugly clumsy thing when it was done, and only burned red like other earthenware, yet it was hard and firm, and would draw the smoke. I was exceedingly comforted with it, for I had always been used to smoke.

I began now to perceive my powder abated considerably; this was a want which it was impossible for me to supply, and I began seriously to consider what I must do when I should have no more powder, that is to say, how I should do to kill any goats. I had, as is observed, in the third year of my being here, kept a young kid and bred her up tame, and I was in hopes of getting a he-goat; but I could not by any means bring it to pass, till my kid grew an old goat, and as I could never find in my heart to kill her, she died at last of mere age.

SECTION XVI

HE REARS A FLOCK OF GOATS—HIS DAIRY—HIS DOMESTIC HABITS AND STYLE OF LIVING—INCREASING PROSPERITY

BEING now in the eleventh year of my residence, and as I have said, my ammunition growing low, I set myself to study some art to trap and snare the goats, to see whether I could not catch some of them alive. I dug several large pits in the earth, in places where I had observed the goats used to feed, and over those pits I placed hurdles, of my own making too, with a great weight upon them; and several times I put ears of barley and dry rice, without setting the trap; and I could easily perceive that the goats had gone in and eaten up the corn, for I could see the marks of their feet. At length I set three traps in one night, and going the next morning, I found them all standing, and yet the bait eaten and gone. This was very discouraging; however, I altered my traps and one morning I found in one of them a large old he-goat, and in one of the others three kids, a male and two females.

As to the old one I knew not what to do with him, he was so fierce I durst not go into the pit to him; that is to say, to go about to bring him away alive, which was what I wanted. I could have killed him, but that was not my business nor would it answer my end; so I even let him out, and he ran away as if he had been frightened out of his wits. I went to the three kids and taking them one by one, I tied them with strings together and with some difficulty brought them all home.

It was a good while before they would feed; but throwing them some sweet corn it tempted them, and they began to be tame. And now I found that if I expected to supply myself with goats' flesh when I had no powder or shot left, breeding some up tame was my only way; when, perhaps, I might have them about my house like a flock of sheep. But then it occurred to me, that I must keep the tame from the wild, or else they would always run wild when they grew up; and the only way for this was, to have some enclosed piece of ground, well fenced, either with hedge or pale to keep them in so effectually, that those within might not break out, or those without break in.

But this was not all, for now I not only had goats' flesh to feed on when I pleased, but milk too; a thing which, indeed, in the beginning I did not so much as think of, and which, when it came into my thoughts, was really an agreeable surprise; for now I set up my dairy, and had sometimes a gallon or two of milk in a day. And as Nature who gives supplies of food to every creature, dictates even naturally how to make use of it, so I, that had never milked a cow, much less a goat, or seen butter or cheese made, only when I was a boy, after a great many essays and miscarriages, made me both butter and cheese at last, and also salt (though I found it partly made to my hand by the heat of the sun upon some of the rocks of the sea), and never wanted it afterwards.

It would have made a stoic smile to have seen me and my little family sit down to dinner. There was my majesty, the prince and lord of the whole island; I had the lives of all my subjects at my absolute command; I could hang, draw, give liberty and take it away, and no rebels among all my subjects.

Then to see how like a king I dined too, all alone, attended by my servants; Poll, as if he had been my favourite, was the only person permitted to talk to me. My dog, who was now grown very old and crazy, and two cats, one on one side of the table and one on the other, expecting now and then a bit from my hand, as a mark of special favour.

My own figure was uncouth enough. I had a great high shapeless cap, made of a goat's skin, with a flap hanging down behind as well to keep the sun from me as to shoot the rain off from running into my neck, nothing being so hurtful in these climates as the rain upon the flesh under the clothes.

I had a short jacket of goat's skin, the skirts coming down to about the middle of the thighs, and a pair of open-kneed breeches of the same; the breeches were made of the skin of an old he-goat, whose hair hung down such a length on either side, that, like pantaloons, it reached to the middle of my legs; stockings and shoes I had none, but had made me a pair of somethings, I scarce know what to call them, like buskins, to flap over my legs, and lace on either side like spatterdashes, but of a most barbarous shape, as indeed were all the rest of my clothes.

I had on a broad belt of goat's skin dried, which I drew together with two thongs of the same, instead of buckles; and in a kind of frog on either side of this, instead of a sword and dagger, hung a little saw and a hatchet; one on one side and one on the other. I had another belt, not so broad, and fastened in the same manner, which hung over my shoulder; and at the end of it under my left arm, hung two pouches, both made of goat's skin too, in one of which hung my powder, in the other my shot. At my back I carried my basket, and on my shoulder my gun; and over my head a great clumsy ugly goat's skin umbrella, but which, after all, was the most necessary thing I had about me, next to my gun. As for my face, the colour of it was not so mulatto-like as one might expect from a man not at all careful of it, and living within nine or ten degrees of the equinox. My beard I had once suffered to grow till it was about a quarter of a yard long; but as I had both scissors and razors sufficient, I had cut it pretty short, except what grew on my upper lip, which I had trimmed into a large pair of Mahometan whiskers, such as I had seen worn by some Turks at Sallee, for the Moors did not wear such, though the Turks did; of these moustachios or whiskers, I will not say they were long enough to hang my hat upon them, but they were of a length and shape monstrous enough, and such as in England would have passed for frightful.

You are to understand, that now I had, as I may call it, two plantations in the island; one my little fortification or tent with the wall about it, under the rock, with the cave behind me, which by this time I had enlarged into several apartments or caves, one within another. One of these, which was the driest and largest, and had a door out beyond my wall or fortification, that is to say, beyond where my wall joined to the rock, was all filled up with the large earthen pots, of which I have given an account, and with fourteen or fifteen great baskets, which would hold five or six bushels each, where I laid up my stores of provision, especially my corn, some in the ear, cut off short from the straw, and the other rubbed out with my hand.

As for my wall, made, as before, with long stakes or piles, those piles grew all like trees, and were by this time grown so big and spread so very much, that there was not the least appearance, to any one's view of any habitation behind them.

Near this dwelling of mine, but a little farther within the land, and upon lower ground, lay my two pieces of corn land, which I kept and duly cultivated and sowed, and which duly yielded me their harvest in its season, and whenever I had occasion for more corn, I had more land adjoining as fit as that.

Besides this, I had my country seat, and I had now a tolerable plantation there also; for, first, I had my little bower, as I called it, which I kept in repair; that is to say, I kept the hedge which encircled it in constantly fitting up to its usual height, the ladder standing always in the inside: I kept the trees, which at first were no more than my stakes, but were now grown very firm and tall, always cut, so that they might spread and grow thick and wild and make the more agreeable shade, which they did effectually to my mind. In the middle of this I had my tent always standing, being a piece of sail spread over poles, set up for that purpose, and which never wanted any repair or renewing; and under this I had made me a squab or couch, with the skins of the creatures I had killed, and with other soft things; and a blanket laid on them, such as belonged to our sea beddings, which I had saved, and a great watch-coat to cover me; and here, whenever I had occasion to be absent from my chief seat, I took up my country habitation.

SECTION XVII

UNEXPECTED ALARM AND CAUSE FOR APPREHENSION—HE FORTIFIES HIS ABODE

It happened one day, about noon, going towards my boat, I was exceedingly surprised with the print of a man's naked foot on the shore, which was very plain to be seen in the sand. I stood like one thunderstruck, or as if I had seen an apparition; I listened, I looked round me, but I could hear nothing, nor see anything; I went up to a rising ground to look farther; I went up the shore and down the shore, but it was all one; I could see no other impression but that one. I went to it again to see if there were any more, and to observe if it might not be my fancy; but there was no room for that, for there was exactly the print of a foot, toes, heel, and every part of a foot: how it came thither I knew not, nor could I in the least imagine; but, after innumerable fluttering thoughts, like a man perfectly confused and out of myself, I came home to my fortification, not feeling, as we say, the ground I went on, but terrified to the last degree;

looking behind me at every two or three steps, mistaking every bush and tree, and fancying every stump at a distance to be a man. Nor is it possible to describe how many various shapes my affrighted imagination represented things to me in, how many wild ideas were found every moment in my fancy, and what strange unaccountable whimsies came into my thoughts by the way.

When I came to my castle (for so I think I called it ever after this), I fled into it like one pursued; whether I went over by the ladder, as first contrived, or went in at the hole in the rock, which I had called a door, I cannot remember; no, nor could I remember the next morning; for never frightened hare fled to cover, or fox to earth with more terror of mind than I to this retreat.

I presently concluded that it must be some of the savages of the main land over against me, who had wandered out to sea in their canoes, and, either driven by the currents or by contrary winds, had made the island, and had been on shore, but were gone away again to sea; being as loth, perhaps, to have stayed in this desolate island as I would have been to have had them.

In the middle of these cogitations, apprehensions and reflections, it came into my thoughts one day, that all this might be a mere chimera of my own, and that this foot might be the print of my foot, when I came on shore from my boat; this cheered me up a little too, and I began to persuade myself it was all a delusion, that it was nothing else but my own foot: and why might I not come that way from the boat, as well as I was going that way to the boat? Again, I considered also, that I could by no means tell for certain where I had trod, and where I had not: and that if, at last, this was only the print of my own foot, I had played the part of those fools, who try to make stories of spectres and apparitions, and then are frightened at them more than anybody.

Now I began to take courage, and to peep abroad again, for I had not stirred out of my castle for three days and nights, so that I began to starve for provisions; for I had little or nothing within doors but some barley cakes and water: then I knew that my goats wanted to be milked too, which usually was my evening diversion; and the poor creatures were in great pain and inconvenience for want of it: and, indeed, it almost spoiled some of them and almost dried up their milk. Encouraging myself, therefore, with the belief that this was nothing but the print of one of my own feet, and that I might be truly said to start at my own shadow, I began to go abroad again, and went to my country house to milk my flock: but to see with what fear I went forward, how often I looked behind me, how I was ready, every now and then, to lay down my basket, and run for my life, it would have made any one think I was haunted with an evil conscience, or that I had been lately most terribly frightened; and so, indeed, I had. However, as I went down thus two or three days, and having seen nothing, I began to be a little bolder, and to think there was really nothing in it but my own imagination; but I could not persuade myself fully of this till I should go down to the shore again, and see this print of a foot, and measure it by my own, and see if there was any similitude or fitness, that I might be assured it was my own foot: but when I came to the place, first, it appeared evidently to me, that when I laid up my boat, I could not possibly be on shore anywhere thereabout: secondly, when I came to measure the mark with my own foot, I found my foot not so large by a great deal. Both these things filled my head with new imaginations, and gave me the vapours again to the highest degree, so that I shook with cold like one in an ague; and I went home again, filled with the belief that some man or men had been on shore there; or in short, that the island was inhabited, and I might be surprised before I was aware; and what course to take for my security, I knew not.

Now I began sorely to repent that I had dug my cave so large as to bring a door through again, which door, as I said, came out beyond where my fortification joined to the rock: upon maturely considering this, therefore, I resolved to draw me a second fortification, in the same manner of a semicircle, at a distance from my wall, just where I had planted a double row of trees about twelve years before, of which I made mention: these trees having been planted so thick before, they wanted but few piles to be driven between them, that they might be thicker and stronger, and my wall would be soon finished: so that I had now a double wall; and my outer was thickened

D

with pieces of timber, old cables, and everything I could think of, to make it strong, having in it seven little holes, about as big as I might put my arm out at. In the inside of this I thickened my wall to about ten feet thick, with continually bringing earth out of my cave, and laying it at the foot of the wall, and walking upon it; and through the seven holes I contrived to plant the muskets, of which I took notice that I had got seven on shore out of the ship; these I planted like my cannon, and fitted them into frames, that held them like a carriage, so that I could fire all the seven guns in two minutes' time: this wall I was many a weary month in finishing, and yet never thought myself safe till it was done.

When this was done, I stuck all the ground without my wall, for a great length every way, as full with stakes, or sticks, of the osier-like wood, which I found so apt to grow, as they could well stand, insomuch, that I believe I might set in near twenty thousand of them, leaving a pretty large space between them and my wall, that I might have room to see an enemy, and they might have no shelter from the young trees if they attempted to approach my outer wall.

Thus, in two years' time, I had a thick grove; and in five or six years' time I had a wood before my dwelling growing so monstrous thick and strong, that it was indeed perfectly impassable; and no men, of what kind soever, would ever imagine that there was anything beyond it, much less a habitation. As for the way in which I proposed to myself to go in and out (for I left no avenue), it was by setting two ladders, one to a part of the rock which was low, and then broke in, and left room to place another ladder upon that; so when the two ladders were taken down, no man living could come down to me without doing himself mischief; and if they had come down, they were still on the outside of my outer wall.

Thus I took all the measures human prudence could suggest for my own preservation; and it will be seen, at length, that they were not altogether without just reason, though I foresaw nothing at that time more than my mere fear suggested to me.

While this was doing, I was not altogether careless of my other affairs; for I had a great concern for my little herd of goats; they were not only a ready supply to me on every occasion, and began to be sufficient for me, without the expense of powder and shot, but also without the fatigue of hunting after the wild ones; and I was loth to lose the advantage of them, and to have them all to nurse up over again.

For this purpose, after long consideration, I could think of but two ways to preserve them; one was, to find another convenient place to dig a cave under ground, and to drive them into it every night; and the other was, to enclose two or three little bits of land, remote from one another, and as much concealed as I could, where I might keep about half a dozen young goats in each place; so that if any disaster happened to the flock in general, I might be able to raise them again with little trouble and time; and this, though it would require a great deal of time and labour, I thought was the most rational design.

Accordingly, I spent some time to find out the most retired parts of the island; and I pitched upon one, which was as private, indeed, as my heart could wish for; it was a little damp piece of ground, in the middle of the hollow and thick woods, where as is observed, I almost lost myself once before, endeavouring to come back that way from the eastern part of the island. Here I found a clear piece of land, near three acres, so surrounded with woods, that it was almost an enclosure by nature; at least it did not want near so much labour to make it so as the other pieces of ground I had worked so hard at.

SECTION XVIII

PRECAUTIONS AGAINST SURPRISE—ROBINSON DISCOVERS THAT HIS ISLAND HAS BEEN VISITED BY CANNIBALS

I IMMEDIATELY went to work with this piece of ground, and in less than a month's time I had so fenced it round, that my flock, or herd, call it which you please, who were not so wild now as at first they might be supposed to be, were well enough secured in it; so, without any further delay, I removed ten young she-goats, and two he-goats to this piece; and when they were there I continued to perfect the fence, till I had made it as secure as the other, which, however, I did at more leisure, and it took me up more time by a great deal. All this labour I was at the expense of purely from my apprehensions on the account of the print of a man's foot which I had seen; for, as yet, I never saw any human creature come near the island; and I had now lived two years under this uneasiness, which, indeed, made my life much less comfortable than it was before, as may be well imagined by any one who knows what it is to live in the constant snare of the fear of man.

After I had thus secured one part of my little living stock, I went about the whole island, searching for another private place to make such another deposit; when, wandering more to the west point of the island than I had ever done yet, and looking out to sea, I thought I saw a boat upon the sea, at a great distance. I had found a perspective glass or two in one of the seamen's chests, which I saved out of our ship, but I had it not about me; and this was so remote, that I could not tell what to make of it, though I looked at it till my eyes were not able to look any longer; whether it was a boat or not, I did not know, but as I descended from the hill I could see no more of it, so I gave it over; only I resolved to go no more out without a perspective glass in my pocket. When I was come down the hill to the end of the island, where, indeed, I had never been before, I was presently convinced that the seeing the print of a man's foot was not such a strange thing in the island as I imagined; and, but that it was a special providence that I was cast upon the side of the island where the savages never came, I should easily have known that nothing was more frequent than for the canoes from the main, when they happened to be too far out at sea, to shoot over to that side of the island for harbour; likewise, as they often met and fought in their canoes, the victors having taken any prisoners, would bring them over to this shore, where, according to their dreadful customs, being all cannibals, they would kill and eat them; of which hereafter.

When I was come down the hill to the shore, as I said above, being the south-west point of the island, I was perfectly confounded and amazed; nor is it possible for me to express the horror of my mind, at seeing the shore spread with skulls, hands, feet, and other bones of human bodies; and, particularly, I observed a place where there had been a fire made, and a circle dug in the earth, like a cockpit, where I supposed the savage wretches had sat down to their inhuman feastings upon the bodies of their fellow-creatures.

I was so astonished with the sight of these things, that I entertained no notions of any danger to myself from it for a long while; all my apprehensions were buried in the thoughts of such a pitch of inhuman brutality and the horror of the degeneracy of human nature, which, though I had heard of it often, yet I never had so near a view of before.

When I came a little out of that part of the island, I stood still awhile, as amazed, and then recovering myself, I looked up with the utmost affection of my soul, and with a flood of tears in my eyes, gave God thanks, that had cast my first lot in a part of the world where I was distinguished from such dreadful creatures as these; and that, though I had esteemed my present condition very miserable, had yet given me so many comforts in it, that I had still more to give thanks for than to complain of: and this, above all, that I had, even in this miserable condition, been comforted with the knowledge of Himself, and the hope of His blessing, which was a felicity more than sufficiently equivalent to all the misery I had suffered or could suffer.

I could not think of ever making any more attempts to bring the other boat round the island to me, lest I should meet with some of these creatures at sea: in which case, if I had happened to have fallen into their hands, I knew what would have been my lot.

Time, and the satisfaction I had that I was in no danger of being discovered by these people, began to wear off my uneasiness about them; and I began to live just in the same composed manner as before, only with this difference, that I used more caution, and kept my eyes more about me, than I did before, lest I should happen to be seen by any of them; and particularly, I was more cautious of firing my gun, lest any of them being on the island should happen to hear it.

It would take up a larger volume than this whole work

is intended to be, to set down all the contrivances I hatched, or rather brooded upon, in my thoughts, for the destroying these creatures, or at least frightening them so as to prevent their coming hither any more.

Sometimes I thought of digging a hole under the place where they made their fire, and putting in five or six pounds of gunpowder, which, when they kindled their fire, would consequently take fire, and blow up all that was near it; but as, in the first place, I should be unwilling to waste so much powder upon them, my store being now within the quantity of one barrel, so neither could I be sure of its going off at a certain time, when it might surprise them: and, at best, that it would little more than just blow the fire about their ears and fright them, but not sufficient to make them forsake the place: so I laid it aside; and then proposed that I would place myself in ambush in some convenient place, with my three guns all double-loaded, and, in the middle of their bloody ceremony, let fly at them, when I should be sure to kill or wound perhaps two or three at every shot: and then falling in upon them with my three pistols and my sword, I made no doubt but that if they were twenty I should kill them all. This fancy pleased my thoughts for some weeks; and I was so full of it, that I often dreamed of it, and sometimes that I was just going to let fly at them in my sleep. I went so far with it in my imagination, that I employed myself several days to find out proper places to put myself in ambuscade, as I said, to watch for them; and I went frequently to the place itself, which was now grown more familiar to me: but while my mind was thus filled with thoughts of revenge, and a putting twenty or thirty of them to the sword as I may call it, the horror I had at the place, and the signals of the barbarous wretches devouring one another, abetted my malice. Well, at length, I found a place in the side of the hill, where I was satisfied I might securely wait till I saw any of their boats coming; and might then, even before they would be ready to come on shore, convey myself, unseen, into some thickets of trees, in one of which there was a hollow large enough to conceal me entirely; and there I might sit and observe all their fearful doings, and take my full aim at their heads, when they were so close together, as that it would be next to impossible that I should miss my shot, or that I should fail wounding three or four of them at the first shot. In this place, then, I resolved to fix my design; and, accordingly, I prepared two muskets and my ordinary fowling-piece. The two muskets I loaded with a brace of slugs each, and four or five small bullets, about the size of pistol-bullets; and the fowling-piece I loaded with near a handful of swan-shot, of the largest size: I also loaded my pistols with four bullets each; and in this posture, well provided with ammunition for a second and third charge, I prepared myself for my expedition.

After I had thus laid the scheme of my design, and, in my imagination, put it in practice, I continually made my tour every morning up to the top of the hill, which was from my castle, as I called it, about three miles, or more, to see if I could observe any boats upon the sea, coming near the island or standing over towards it; but I began to tire of this hard duty, after I had, for two or three months, constantly kept my watch, but came always back without any discovery: there having not, in all that time, been the least appearance, not only on or near the shore, but on the whole ocean, so far as my eyes or glasses could reach every way.

When I began to be weary of the fruitless excursion, which I had made so long and so far every morning in vain, so my opinion of the action itself began to alter; and I began, with cooler and calmer thoughts, to consider what I was going to engage in: what authority or call I had to pretend to be judge and executioner upon these men as criminals, whom Heaven had thought fit for so many ages, to suffer unpunished to go on and to be as it were, the executioners of His judgments one upon another.

SECTION XIX

ROBINSON DISCOVERS A CAVE, WHICH SERVES HIM AS A RETREAT AGAINST THE SAVAGES

In this disposition I continued for near a year after this. I kept myself more retired than ever, and seldom went from my cell, except upon my constant employment, viz., to milk my she-goats, and manage my little flock in the wood, which, as it was quite on the other part of the island, was quite out of danger; for certain it is, that these savage people, who sometimes haunted this island, never came with any thoughts of finding anything here, and consequently never wandered off from the coast; and I doubt not but they might have been several times on shore after my apprehensions of them had made me cautious, as well as before.

I believe the reader of this will not think it strange if I confess that these anxieties, these constant dangers I lived in, and the concern that was now upon me, put an end to all invention, and to all the contrivances that I had laid for my future accommodations and conveniences. I had the care of my safety more now upon my hands than that of my food. I cared not to drive a nail, or chop a stick of wood now, for fear the noise I might make should be heard; much less would I fire a gun, for the same reason: and above all, I was intolerably uneasy at making any fire, lest the smoke, which is visible at a great distance in the day, should betray me. For this reason, I removed that part of my business which required fire, such as burning of pots, pipes, etc., into my new apartment in the woods; where, after I had been some time, I found, to my unspeakable consolation, a mere natural cave in the earth, which went in a vast way, and where, I dare say, no savage, had he been at the mouth of it, would be so hardy as to venture in: nor, indeed, would any man else, but one who, like me, wanted nothing so much as a safe retreat.

While I was cutting down some wood here, I perceived that behind a very thick branch of low brushwood, or underwood, there was a kind of hollow place: I was curious to look in it, and getting with difficulty into the mouth of it, I found it was pretty large: that is to say, sufficient for me to stand upright in it, and perhaps another with me: but I must confess to you that I made more haste out than I did in, when, looking farther into the place, and which was perfectly dark, I saw two broad shining eyes of some creature, which twinkled like two stars, the dim light from the cave's mouth shining directly in, and making the reflection. Plucking up my courage, I took up a firebrand, and in I rushed again, with the stick flaming in my hand: I had not gone three steps in, but I was almost as much frightened as I was before; for I heard a very loud sigh, like that of a man in some pain, and it was followed by a broken noise, as of words half expressed, and then a deep sigh again. I stepped back, and was indeed struck with such a surprise, that it put me into a cold sweat; and if I had had a hat on my head, I will not answer for it, that my hair might not have lifted it off. But still plucking up my spirits as well as I could, and encouraging myself a little with considering that the power and presence of God was everywhere, and was able to protect me, upon this I stepped forward again, and by the light of the firebrand, holding it up a little over my head, I saw lying on the ground a most monstrous, frightful old he-goat, just making his will, as we say, and gasping for life, and dying, indeed, of mere old age. I stirred him a little to see if I could get him out, and he essayed to get up, but was not able to raise himself; and I thought with myself he might even lie there; for if he had frightened me, so he would certainly fright any of the savages, if any of them should be so hardy as to come in there while he had any life in him.

I was now recovered from my surprise, and began to look round me, when I found the cave was but very small, that is to say, it might be about twelve feet over, but in no manner of shape, neither round nor square, no hands having ever been employed in making it but those of Nature. I observed also that there was a place at the farther side of it that went in farther, but was so low that it required me to creep upon my hands and knees to go into it, and whither it went I knew not: so having no candle I gave it over for that time; but resolved to come again the next day, provided with candles and a tinder-box, which I had made of the lock of one of the muskets, with some wild-fire in the pan.

Accordingly, the next day I came provided with six large candles of my own making (for I made very good candles now of goat's tallow, but was hard set for candle-wick, using sometimes rags or rope-yarn, and sometimes the dried rind of a reed-like nettle); and going into this low place, I was obliged to creep upon all fours, as I have said, almost ten yards; which, by the way, I thought was a venture bold enough, considering that I knew not how far it might go, nor what was beyond it. When I had got through the strait, I found the roof rose higher up, I believe near twenty feet; but never was such a glorious sight seen in the island, I dare say, as it was, to look round the sides and roof of this vault or cave; the wall reflected a hundred thousand lights to me from my two candles. What it was in the rock, whether diamonds, or any other precious stones, or gold, which I rather supposed it to be, I knew not. The place I was in was a most delightful cavity or grotto of its kind, as could be expected, though perfectly dark; the floor was dry and level, and had a sort of small loose gravel upon it, so that there was no nauseous or venomous creature to be seen, neither was there any damp or wet on the sides or roof: the only difficulty in it was the entrance; which, however, as it was a place of security, and such a retreat as I wanted, I thought that was a convenience; so that I was really rejoiced at the discovery, and resolved, without any delay, to bring some of those things which I was most anxious about to this place; particularly, I resolved to bring hither my magazine of powder and all my spare arms, viz., two fowling-pieces, for I had three in all, and three muskets, for of them I had eight in all: so I kept at my castle only five, which stood ready mounted like pieces of cannon on my outmost fence, and were ready also to take out upon any expedition. Upon this occasion of removing my ammunition, I happened to open the barrel of powder which I took up out of the sea and which had been wet; and I found that the water had penetrated about three or four inches into the powder on every side, which caking and growing hard, had preserved the inside like a kernel in the shell; so that I had near sixty pounds of very good powder in the centre of the cask: this was a very agreeable discovery to me at that time; so I carried all away thither, never keeping above two or three pounds of powder with me in my castle, for fear of a surprise of any kind: I also carried thither all the lead I had left for bullets.

I fancied myself now like one of the ancient giants, which were said to live in caves and holes in the rocks, where none could come at them; for I persuaded myself, while I was here, that if five hundred savages were to hunt me, they could never find me out; or, if they did, they would not venture to attack me here. The old goat, whom I found expiring, died in the mouth of the cave next day after I made this discovery and I found it much easier to dig a great hole there, and throw him in and cover him with earth, than to drag him out; so I interred him there, to prevent offence to my nose.

I was now in the twenty-third year of my residence in this island; and was so naturalised to the place, and the manner of living, that could I have but enjoyed the certainty that no savages would come to the place to disturb me, I could have been content to have capitulated for spending the rest of my time there, even to the last moment, till I had laid me down and died, like the old goat in the cave. I had also arrived to some little diversions and amusements, which made the time pass a great deal more pleasantly with me than it did before; as, first, I had taught my Poll, as I noted before, to speak; and he did it so familiarly, and talked so articulately and plain, that it was very pleasant to me; for I believe no bird ever spoke plainer; and he lived with me no less than six-and-twenty years: how long he might have lived afterwards I know not, though I know they have a notion in the Brazils that they live a hundred years. My dog was a very pleasant and loving companion to me for no less than sixteen years of my time, and then died of mere old age. As for my cats, they multiplied to that degree, that I was obliged to shoot several of them at first, to keep them from devouring me and all I had; but at length, when the two old ones I brought with me were gone, and after some time continually driving them from me, and letting them have no provision with me, they all ran wild into the woods, except two or three favourites, which I kept tame, and whose young, when they had any, I always drowned; and these were part of my family. Besides these, I always kept two or three household kids about me, whom I taught to feed out of my hand; and I had two more parrots, which talked pretty well, and would all call Robin Crusoe, but none like my first; nor, indeed, did I take the pains with any of them that I had done with him. I had also several tame sea-fowls, whose names I knew not, that I caught upon the shore, and cut their wings; and the little stakes which I had planted before my castle wall being now grown up to a good thick grove, these fowls all lived among these low trees, and bred there, which was very agreeable to me: so that, as I said above, I began to be very well contented with the life I led, if I could have been secured from the dread of the savages.

SECTION XX

ANOTHER VISIT OF THE SAVAGES—ROBINSON SEES THEM DANCING—PERCEIVES THE WRECK OF A VESSEL

It was now the month of December, as I said above, in my twenty-third year; and this being the southern solstice (for winter I cannot call it), was the particular time of my harvest, and required my being much abroad in the fields; when going out pretty early in the morning, even before it was thorough daylight, I was surprised with seeing a light of some fire upon the shore, at a distance from me of about two miles, towards the end of the island where I had observed some savages had been, as before; and not on the other side, but, to my great affliction, it was on my side of the island.

I was indeed terribly surprised at the sight, and stopped short within my grove, not daring to go out, lest I might be surprised; and yet I had no more peace within, from the apprehensions I had that if these savages, in rambling over the island, should find my corn standing or cut, or any of my works and improvements, they would immediately conclude that there were people in the place, and would then never give over till they had found me out. In this extremity, I went back directly to my castle, pulled up the ladder after me, and made all things without look as wild and as natural as I could.

Then I prepared myself within, putting myself in a posture of defence: I loaded all my cannon, as I called them, that is to say, my muskets, which were mounted upon my new fortification, and all my pistols, and resolved to defend myself to the last gasp; not forgetting seriously to commend myself to the divine protection, and earnestly to pray to God to deliver me out of the hands of the barbarians. I continued in this posture about two hours; and began to be mighty impatient for intelligence abroad, for I had no spies to send out. After sitting awhile longer, and musing what I should do in this case, I was not able to bear sitting in ignorance any longer; so setting up my ladder to the side of the hill, where there was a flat place, as I observed before, and then pulling the ladder up after me, I set it up again, and mounted to the top of the hill, and pulling out my perspective glass, which I had taken on purpose, I laid me down flat on the ground, and began to look for the place. I presently found there were no less than nine naked savages, sitting round a small fire they had made, not to warm them, for they had no need of that, the weather being extremely hot, but, as I supposed, to dress some of their barbarous diet of human flesh, which they had brought with them, whether alive or dead I could not tell.

They had two canoes with them, which they had hauled up upon the shore; and as it was then tide of ebb, they seemed to me to wait for the return of the flood to go away again. It is not easy to imagine what confusion this sight put me into, especially seeing them come on my side of the island, and so near me too, but when I considered their coming must be always with the current of the ebb, I began afterwards, to be more sedate in my mind, being satisfied that I might go abroad with safety all the time of the tide of flood, if they were not on shore before; and having made this observation, I went abroad about my harvest work with the more composure.

As I expected, so it proved, for as soon as the tide made to the westward, I saw them all take boat and row (or paddle, as we call it) away. I should have observed, that for an hour or more before they went off, they went a dancing; and I could easily discern their postures and gestures by my glass. I could not perceive, by my nicest observation, but that they were stark naked and had not the least covering upon them; but whether they were men or women, I could not distinguish.

As soon as I saw them shipped and gone, I took two guns upon my shoulders, and two pistols in my girdle, and my great sword by my side, without a scabbard, and with all the speed I was able to make, went away to the hill where I had discovered the first appearance of all; and as soon as I got thither, which was not in less than two hours (for I could not go apace, being so loaden with arms as I was), I perceived there had been three canoes more of savages at that place; and looking out farther, I saw they were all at sea together, making over for the main. This was a dreadful sight to me, especially as, going down to the shore, I could see the marks of horror, which the dismal work they had been about had left behind it, viz., the blood, the bones, and part of the flesh, of human bodies, eaten and devoured by those wretches with merriment and sport. I wore out a year and three months more before I ever saw any more of the savages.

The perturbation of my mind, during this fifteen months' interval was very great; I slept unquiet, dreamed always frightful dreams, and often started out of my sleep in the night; in the day, great troubles overwhelmed my mind; and in the night, I dreamed often of killing the savages, and of the reason why I might justify the doing of it. It was in the middle of May, on the sixteenth day, I think, as well as my poor wooden calendar would reckon, for I marked all upon the post still; I say, it was on the sixteenth of May that it blew a very great storm of wind all day, with a great deal of lightning and thunder, and a very foul night it was after it. I knew not what was the particular occasion of it, but as I was reading in the Bible, and taken up with very serious thoughts about my present condition, I was surprised with the noise of a gun, as I thought, fired at sea. This was, to be sure, a surprise quite of a different nature from any I had met with before; for the notions this put into my thoughts were quite of another kind. I started up in the greatest haste imaginable, and, in a trice, clapped my ladder to the middle place of the rock, and pulled it after me, and mounting it the second time, got to the top of the hill the very moment that a flash of fire bid me listen for a second gun, which accordingly, in about half a minute, I heard; and, by the sound, knew that it was from that part of the sea where I was driven down the current in my boat. I immediately considered that this must be some ship in distress, and that they had some comrade or some other ship in company, and fired these guns for signals of distress and to obtain help. I had the presence of mind, at that minute, to think that though I could not help them, it might be they might help me: so I brought together all the dry wood I could get at hand, and making a good handsome pile, I set it on fire upon the hill. The wood was dry, and blazed freely; and though the wind blew very hard, yet it burnt fairly out: so that I was certain, if there was any such thing as a ship, they must needs see it: and no doubt they did; for as soon as ever my fire blazed up I heard another gun, and after that several others, all from the same quarter. I plied my fire all night long, till daybreak; and when it was broad day, and the air cleared up, I saw something at a great distance at sea, full east of the island, whether a sail or a hull I could not distinguish, no, not with my glass; the distance was so great and the weather still something hazy also; at least it was so out at sea.

I looked frequently at it all that day, and soon perceived that it did not move; so I presently concluded that it was a ship at anchor; and being eager, you may be sure, to be satisfied, I took my gun in my hand, and ran towards the south side of the island, to the rocks where I had formerly been carried away with the current; and getting up there, the weather by this time being perfectly clear, I could plainly see, to my great sorrow, the wreck of a ship, cast away in the night upon those concealed rocks which I found when I was out in my boat; and which rocks, as they checked the violence of the stream, and made a kind of counter-stream, or eddy, were the occasion of my recovering from the most desperate, hopeless condition that ever I had been in, in all my life. Thus, what is one man's safety is another man's destruction; for it seems these men, whoever they were, being out of their knowledge, and the rocks being wholly under water, had been driven upon them in the night, the wind blowing hard at E.N.E. Had they seen the island, as I must necessarily suppose they did not, they must, as I thought, have endeavoured to have saved themselves on shore by the help of their boat; but their firing off guns for help, especially when they saw, as I imagined, my fire, filled me with many thoughts: First, I imagined that upon seeing my light, they might have put themselves into their boat, and endeavoured to make the shore; but that the sea going very high, they might have been cast away: other times I imagined that they might have lost their boat before, as might be the case many ways; as particularly, by the breaking of the sea upon their ship, which many times obliges men to stave, or take in pieces, their boat, and sometimes to throw it overboard with their own hands: other times I imagined they had some other ship or ships in company, who upon the signals of distress they had made, had taken them up and carried them off: other times I fancied they were all gone off to sea in their boat, and being hurried away by the current that I had been formerly in, were carried out into the great ocean, where there was nothing but misery and perishing; and that perhaps they might by this time be starving, and in a condition to think of eating one another.

SECTION XXI

HE VISITS THE WRECK AND OBTAINS MANY STORES FROM IT —AGAIN THINKS OF QUITTING THE ISLAND

TILL the last year of my being on this island, I never knew whether any were saved out of that ship or no; and had only the affliction, some days after, to see the corpse of a drowned boy come on shore at the end of the island which was next the shipwreck. He had no clothes on but a seaman's waistcoat, a pair of open-kneed linen drawers, and a blue linen shirt; but nothing to direct me so much as to guess what nation he was of: he had nothing in his pockets but two pieces of eight and a tobacco pipe; the last was to me of ten times more value than the first.

It was now calm, and I had a great mind to venture out in my boat to this wreck, not doubting but I might find something on board that might be useful to me: but that did not altogether press me so much as the possibility that there might be yet some living creature on board, whose life I might not only save, but might, by saving that life, comfort my own to the last degree. And this thought clung so to my heart that I could not be quiet night or day, but I must venture out in my boat on board this wreck; and committing the rest to God's providence, I thought the impression was so strong upon my mind that it could not be resisted, that it must come from some invisible direction, and that I should be wanting to myself if I did not go.

Under the power of this impression, I hastened back to my castle, prepared everything for my voyage, took a quantity of bread, a great pot of fresh water, a compass to steer by, a bottle of rum (for I had still a great deal of that left) and a basket of raisins; and thus loading myself with everything necessary, I went down to my boat, got the water out of her, put her afloat, loaded all my cargo in her, and then went home again for more. My second cargo was a great bag of rice, the umbrella to set up over my head for a shade, another large pot of fresh water, and about two dozen of my small loaves, or barley-cakes, more than before, with a bottle of goat's milk and a cheese: all which with great labour and sweat I carried to my boat; and praying to God to direct my voyage, I put out; and rowing, or paddling, the canoe along the shore, came at last to the utmost point of the island on the north-east side.

Having hauled my boat into a little creek on the shore, I stepped out, and sat me down upon a rising bit of ground, very pensive and anxious, between fear and desire, about my voyage: when, as I was musing, I could perceive that the tide was turned, and the flood come on; upon which my going was impracticable for so many hours.

I resolved, the next morning, to set out with the first of the tide; and reposing myself for the night in my canoe, under the great watch-coat I mentioned, I launched out. I went at a great rate directly for the wreck, and in less than two hours I came up to it. It was a dismal sight to look at; the ship, which, by its building, was Spanish, stuck fast, jammed in between two rocks; all the stern and quarter of her were beaten to pieces with the sea; and as her forecastle, which stuck in the rocks, had run on with great violence, her mainmast and foremast was brought by the board, that is to say, broken short off; but her bowsprit was sound, and the head and bow appeared firm. When I came close to her, a dog appeared upon her, who, seeing me coming, yelped and cried; and as soon as I called him jumped into the sea to come to me. I took him into the boat, but found him almost dead with hunger and thirst. I gave him a cake of my bread, and he devoured it like a ravenous wolf that had been starving a fortnight in the snow. I then gave the poor creature some fresh water, with which, if I would have let him, he would have burst himself. After this I went on board: but the first sight I met with was two men drowned in the cook room, or forecastle of the ship, with their arms fast about one another. I concluded, as indeed probable, that when the ship struck, it being in a storm, the sea broke so high, and so continually over her, that the men were not able to bear it, and were strangled with the constant rushing in of the water, as much as if they had been under water. Besides the dog there was nothing left in the ship that had life; nor any goods, that I could see, but what were spoiled by the water.

I found, however, besides several chests, a little cask full of liquor, of about twenty gallons, which I got into my boat with much difficulty. There were several muskets in the cabin, and a great powder-horn, with about four pounds of powder in it; as for the muskets, I had no occasion for them, so I left them, but took the powder-horn. I took a fire-shovel and tongs, which I wanted extremely; as also two little brass kettles, a copper pot to make chocolate, and a gridiron; and with this cargo, and the dog, I came away, the tide beginning to make home again; and the same evening, about an hour within night, I reached the island again, weary and fatigued to the last degree. I reposed that night in the boat; and in the morning I resolved to harbour what I had got in my new cave, and not carry it home to my castle. After refreshing myself, I got all my cargo on shore, and began to examine the particulars. I found on emptying the chest, among other things, some very good shirts, which were very welcome to me; and about a dozen and a half of white linen handkerchiefs and coloured neckcloths; the former was also very welcome, being exceeding refreshing to wipe my face in a hot day. Upon the whole, I got very little by this voyage that was of any use to me: for, as to some money, I had found I had no manner of occasion for it; it was to me as the dirt under my feet; and I would have given it all for three or four pairs of English shoes and stockings, which were things I greatly wanted, but had none on my feet for many years.

I lived in this condition near two years more; all the time filled with projects and designs, how, if it were possible, I might get away from this island; and I believe verily, if I had the boat that I went from Sallee in, I should have ventured to sea, bound anywhere, I knew not whither.

It was one of the nights of the rainy season in March, the four-and-twentieth year of my first setting foot in this island of solitariness, I was laying in my bed awake. I had no uneasiness of mind more than ordinary, but could by no means close my eyes, that is, so as to sleep; no, not a wink all night long, otherwise than as follows:

I ran over the whole history of my life by abridgment, as I may call it, to my coming to this island; and also since I came to this island. In my reflections upon the state of my case, since I came here, I was comparing the happy posture of my affairs in the first years of my habitation, with the life of anxiety, fear, and care, which I had lived ever since I had seen the print of a foot in the sand.

Then I came to reflect seriously upon the real danger I had been in for so many years; and how I had walked about in the greatest security, and with all possible tranquillity, when perhaps nothing but the brow of a hill, a great tree, or the casual approach of night, had been between me and the worst kind of destruction, viz., that of falling into the hands of cannibals and savages. I would unjustly slander myself, if I should say I was not sincerely thankful to my great Preserver, to whom all these unknown deliverances were due.

I made this conclusion, however, that my only way to go about an attempt for an escape was, if possible, to get a savage into my possession; and, if possible, it should be one of their prisoners whom they had condemned to be eaten, and should bring thither to kill; but these thoughts were still attended with this difficulty, that it was impossible to effect this without attacking a whole caravan of them, and killing them all; and my heart trembled at the thoughts of shedding so much blood, though it was for deliverance.

However, after many disputes with myself, I determined, if possible, to get one of the savages into my hands, cost what it would; so I resolved to put myself upon the watch to see them when they came on shore, and leave the rest to the event.

SECTION XXII

ROBINSON RESCUES ONE OF THEIR CAPTIVES FROM THE SAVAGES, WHOM HE NAMES FRIDAY, AND MAKES HIS SERVANT

About a year and a half after I entertained these notions (and by long musing had, as it were, resolved them into nothing, for want of an occasion to put them into execution), I was surprised, one morning early, with seeing no less than five canoes all on shore together on my side the island, and the people who belonged to them all landed and out of my sight. The number of them broke all my measures; for seeing so many, and knowing that they always came four or six, or sometimes more, in a boat, I could not tell what to think of it, or how to take my measures, to attack twenty or thirty men single-handed; so lay still in my castle, perplexed and discomforted: however, I put myself into all the same postures for an attack that I had formerly provided, and was just ready for action, if anything had presented. Having waited a good while listening to hear if they made any noise, at length, being very impatient, I set my guns at the foot of my ladder, and clambered up to the top of the hill, by my two stages as usual; standing so, however, that my head did not appear above the hill, so that they could not perceive me by any means. Here I observed, by the help of my perspective glass, that they were no less than thirty in number; that they had a fire kindled, and that they had meat dressed. How they had cooked it I know not, or what it was, but they were all dancing, in I know not how many barbarous gestures and figures, their own way, round the fire.

While I was thus looking on them, I perceived, by my perspective, two miserable wretches dragged from the boats, where, it seems, they were laid by, and were now brought out for the slaughter. I perceived one of them immediately fall, being knocked down, I suppose, with a club or wooden sword, for that was their way, and two or three others were at work immediately, cutting him open for their cookery, while the other victim was left standing by himself, till they should be ready for him. In that very moment this poor wretch seeing himself a little at liberty, and unbound, nature inspired him with hopes of life, and he started away from them, and ran with incredible swiftness along the sands, directly towards me, I mean towards that part of the coast where my habitation was. I was dreadfully frightened, I must acknowledge, when I perceived him run my way, and especially when, as I thought, I saw him pursued by the whole body. However, I kept my station, and my spirits began to recover, when I found that there was not above three men that followed him; and still more was I encouraged when I found that he outstripped them exceedingly in running, and gained ground of them, so that if he could but hold it for half an hour, I saw easily he would fairly get away from them all.

There was between them and my castle the creek, which I mentioned often in the first part of my story, where I landed my cargoes out of the ship; and this I saw plainly he must necessarily swim over, or the poor wretch would be taken there; but when the savage escaping came thither he made nothing of it, though the tide was then up; but plunging in, swam through in about thirty strokes, or thereabouts, landed, and ran on with exceeding strength and swiftness. When the three persons came to the creek, I found that two of them could swim, but the third could not, and that, standing on the other side, he looked at the others, but went no farther, and soon after went softly back again; which, as it happened, was very well for him in the end. I observed that the two who swam were yet more than twice as long swimming over the creek as the fellow was that fled from them. It came now very warmly upon my thoughts, and indeed irresistibly, that now was the time to get me a servant, and perhaps a companion or assistant, and that I was called plainly by Providence to save this poor creature's life. I immediately ran down the ladders, with all possible expedition, fetched my two guns, for they were both at the foot of the ladders, as I observed above, and getting up again, with the same haste, to the top of the hill, I crossed toward the sea, and having a very short cut, and all down hill, placed myself in the way between the pursuers and the pursued, hallooing aloud to him that fled, who, looking back, was at first, perhaps, as much frightened at me as at them; but I beckoned with my hand to him to come back; and, in the meantime, I slowly advanced towards the two that followed: then rushing at once upon the foremost, I knocked him down with the stock of my piece. I was loth to fire, because I would not have the rest hear; though at that distance it would not have been easily heard, and being out of sight of the smoke too, they would not have easily known what to make of it. Having knocked this fellow down, the other who pursued him stopped, as if he had been frightened, and I advanced apace towards him: but as I came nearer, I perceived presently he had a bow and arrow, and was fitting it to shoot at me; so I was then necessitated to shoot at him first, which I did, and killed him at the first shot. The poor savage who fled but had stopped, though he saw both his enemies fallen and killed, as he thought, yet was so frightened with the fire and noise of my piece, that he stood stock still, and neither came forward nor went backward, though he seemed rather inclined to fly than to come on. I hallooed again to him to come forward, which he easily understood, and came a little way; then stopped again; and then a little further, and then stopped again, and I could then perceive that he stood trembling, as if he had been taken prisoner, and had just been to be killed, as his two enemies were. I beckoned to him again, to come to me, and gave him all the signs of encouragement that I could think of; and he came nearer and nearer, kneeling down every ten or twelve steps, in token of acknowledgment for having saved his life. I smiled at him, and looked pleasantly, and beckoned to him to come still nearer; at length he came close to me; and then he kneeled down again, kissed the ground, and laid his head upon the ground, and taking me by the foot, set my foot upon his head: this, it seems, was in token of swearing to be my slave for ever. I took him up, and made much of him, and encouraged him all I could. But there was more work to do yet; for I perceived the savage whom I knocked down was not killed but stunned with the blow, and began to come to himself: so I pointed to him, and showed him the savage, that he was not dead; upon this he spoke some words to me, and though I could not understand them, yet I thought they were pleasant to hear; for they were the first sound of a man's voice that I had heard, my own excepted, for above twenty-five years. But there was no time for reflections now; the savage who was knocked down recovered himself so far as to sit up on the ground, and I perceived that my savage began to be afraid; but when I saw that, I presented my other piece at the man, as if I would shoot him: upon this my savage, for so I call him now, made a motion to me to lend him my sword, which hung naked in a belt by my side, which I did. He no sooner had it, but he runs to his enemy, and, at one blow, cut off his head so cleverly, no executioner in Germany could have done it sooner or better: which I thought very strange for one who, I had reason to believe, never saw a sword in his life before, except their own wooden swords; however, it seems, as I learned afterwards, they make their wooden swords so sharp, so heavy, and the wood is so hard, that they will cut off heads even with them, ay, and arms, and that at one blow too. When he had done this, he comes laughing to me, in sign of triumph, and brought me the sword again, and with abundance of gestures, which I did not understand, laid it down. But that which astonished him most was to know how I killed the other Indian so far off; so pointing to him, he made signs to me to let him go to him; so I bade him go as well as I could. When he came to him, he stood like one amazed, looking at him, turning him first on one side, then on the other, looked at the wound the bullet had made, which, it seems, was just in his breast, where it had made a hole, and no great quantity of blood had followed, but he had bled inwardly, for he was quite dead. He took up his bow and arrows, and came back; so I turned to go away, and beckoned him to follow me, making signs to him that more might come after them. Upon this he made signs to me that he should bury them with sand, that they might not be seen by the rest, if they followed; and so I made signs to him again to do so. He fell to work; and, in an instant, he had scraped a hole in the sand with his hands, big enough to bury the first in, and then dragged him into it, and covered him; and did so by the other also; I believe he had buried them both in a quarter of an hour. Then calling him away, I conveyed him, not to my castle, but quite away, to my cave, on the farther part of the island. Here I gave him bread and a bunch of raisins to eat, and a draught of water, which I found he was indeed in great distress for, by his running; and having refreshed him, I made signs for him to go and lie down to sleep; showing him a place where I had laid some rice straw, and a blanket upon it which I used to sleep upon myself sometimes; so the poor creature lay down and went to sleep.

He was a comely, handsome fellow, perfectly well-made, with straight, strong limbs, not too large, tall, and well-shaped, and, as I reckon, about twenty-six years of age. He had a very good countenance, not a fierce and surly aspect; but seemed to have something very manly in his face; and yet he had all the sweetness and softness of a European in his countenance too, especially when he smiled. His hair was long and black, not curled like wool; his forehead was high and large; and a great vivacity and sparkling sharpness in his eyes. The colour of his skin was not quite black, but very tawny; and yet not an ugly, yellow, nauseous tawny, as the Brazilians and Virginians and other natives of America are, but of a bright kind of a dun olive-colour, that had something in it very agreeable, though not very easy to describe. His face was round and plump; his nose small, not flat like the negroes; a very good mouth, thin lips, and his fine teeth well set, and as white as ivory.

After he had slumbered, rather than slept, about half an hour, he awoke again, and came out of the cave to me, for I had been milking my goats, which I had in the enclosure just by; when he espied me, he came running to me, laying himself down again upon the ground, with all the possible signs of an humble, thankful disposition, making a great many antic gestures to show it. At last, he lays his head flat upon the ground, close to my foot, and sets my other foot upon his head, as he had done before; and after this made all the signs to me of subjection, servitude, and submission imaginable, to let me know how he would serve me as long as he lived. I understood him in many things, and let him know I was very well pleased with him. In a little time I began to speak to him and teach him to speak to me; and, first, I let him know his name should be FRIDAY, which was the day I saved his life : I called him so for the memory of the time. I likewise taught him to say Master : and then let him know that was to be my name : I likewise taught him to say Yes and No, and to know the meaning of them. I gave him some milk in an earthen pot, and let him see me drink it before him, and sop my bread in it; and gave him a cake of bread to do the like, which he quickly complied with, and made signs that it was very good for him. I kept there with him all that night; but as soon as it was day, I beckoned to him to come with me, and let him know that I would give him some clothes : at which he seemed very glad, for he was stark naked. As we went by the place where he had buried the two men, he pointed exactly to the spot, and showed me the marks he had made to find them again, making signs to me that we should dig them up again, and eat them. At this I appeared very angry, expressed my abhorrence of it, and beckoned with my hand to him to come away, which he did immediately, with great submission. I then led him up to the top of the hill, to see if his enemies were gone; and pulling out my glass, I looked, and saw plainly the place where they had been, but no appearance of them or their canoes : so that it was plain they were gone, and had left their two comrades behind them, without any search after them.

But I was not content with this discovery; but having now more courage, and consequently more curiosity, I took my man Friday with me, giving him the sword in his hand, with the bow and arrows at his back, which I found he could use very dexterously, making him carry one gun for me, and I two for myself : and away we marched to the place where these creatures had been, for I had a mind now to get some further intelligence of them. When I came to the place my very blood ran chill in my veins, and my heart sunk within me at the horror of the spectacle; indeed, it was a dreadful sight, at least it was to me, though Friday made nothing of it. The place was covered with human bones, the ground dyed with their blood, and great pieces of flesh left here and there, half-eaten, mangled, and scorched; and, in short, all the tokens of the triumphant feast they had been making there, after a victory over their enemies. I saw three skulls, five hands, and the bones of three or four legs and feet, and abundance of other parts of the bodies; and Friday, by his signs, made me understand that they brought over four prisoners to feast upon; that three of them were eaten up, and that he, pointing to himself, was the fourth; that there had been a great battle between them and their next king, whose subjects, it seems, he had been one of, and that they had taken a great number of prisoners; all which were carried to several places by those who had taken them in the fight, in order to feast upon them, as was done here by these wretches upon those they brought hither.

I caused Friday to gather up all the skulls, bones and flesh, and whatever remained, and lay them together in a heap, and make a great fire upon it, and burn them all to ashes. I found Friday had still a hankering stomach after some of the flesh, and was still a cannibal in his nature; but I discovered so much abhorrence at the very thoughts of it, and at the least appearance of it, that he durst not discover it: for I had, by some means, let him know that I would kill him if he offered it.

When he had done this, we came back to our castle; and there I fell to work for my man Friday; and, first of all, I gave him a pair of linen drawers, which I had out of the poor gunner's chest I mentioned which I found in the wreck; and which, with a little alteration, fitted him very well, and then I made him a jerkin of goat's skin, as well as my skill would allow (for I was now grown a tolerable good tailor); and I gave him a good cap, which I made of hare's skin, very convenient and fashionable enough; and thus he was clothed for the present, tolerably well, and was mighty well pleased to see himself almost as well clothed as his master! It is true, he went awkwardly in those clothes at first: wearing the drawers was very awkward to him, and the sleeves of the waistcoat galled his shoulders, and the inside of his arms, but after a little easing them where he complained they hurt him, and using himself to them, he took to them at length very well.

The next day after I came home to my hutch with him, I began to consider where I should lodge him; and that I might do well for him and yet be perfectly easy myself, I made a little tent for him in the vacant place between my two fortifications, in the inside of the last and in the outside of the first. As there was a door of entrance there into my cave, I made a formal framed door-case, and a door to it of boards, and set it up in the passage, a little within the entrance; and causing the door to open in the inside, I barred it up in the night, taking in my ladders too; so that Friday could in no way come at me in the inside of my innermost wall, without making so much noise in getting over that it must needs waken me; for my first wall had now a complete roof over it of long poles, covering all my tent, and leaning up to the side of the hill; which was again laid across with smaller sticks instead of laths, and then thatched over a great thickness with the rice-straw, which was strong, like reeds; and at the hole or place which was left to go in or out by the ladder, I had placed a kind of trap door, which, if it had been attempted on the outside, would not have opened at all, but would have fallen down, and made a great noise; as to weapons, I took them all into my side every night. But I needed none of all this precaution; for never man had a more faithful, loving, sincere servant than Friday was to me; without passions, sullenness, or designs, perfectly obliged and engaged—his very affections were tied to me like those of a child to a father; and I dare say, he would have sacrificed his life for the saving mine upon any occasion whatsoever; the many testimonies he gave me of this put it out of doubt, and soon convinced me that I needed to use no precautions as to my safety on his account.

With my new companion I was greatly delighted, and made it my business to teach him everything that was proper to make him useful, handy, and helpful; but especially to make him speak, and understand me when I spoke; and he was the aptest scholar that ever was; and particularly was so merry, so constantly diligent, and so pleased when he could but understand me, or make me understand him, that it was very pleasant to me to talk to him. Now my life began to be so easy that I began to say to myself, that could I have been safe from more savages, I cared not if I was never to remove from the place where I lived.

SECTION XXIII

ROBINSON INSTRUCTS AND CIVILISES HIS MAN FRIDAY—ENDEAVOURS TO GIVE HIM AN IDEA OF CHRISTIANITY

AFTER I had been two or three days returned to my castle, I thought that in order to bring Friday off from his horrid way of feeding, and from the relish of a cannibal's stomach, I ought to let him taste other flesh; so I took him out with me one morning to the woods. I went, indeed, intending to kill a kid out of my own flock, and bring it home and dress it; but as I was going, I saw a she-goat lying down in the shade, and two young kids sitting by her. I caught hold of Friday: "Hold," said I; "stand still"; and made signs to him not to stir: immediately I presented my piece, shot, and killed one of the kids. The poor creature, who had, at a distance, indeed, seen me kill the savage, his enemy, but did not know, nor could imagine, how it was done, was sensibly surprised, trembled and shook, and looked so amazed, that I thought he would have sunk down. He did not see the kid I shot at, or perceived I had killed it, but ripped up his waistcoat, to feel whether he was not wounded, and as I found presently, thought I was resolved to kill him; for he came and kneeled down to me, and embracing my knees, said a great many things I did not understand; but I could easily see the meaning was to pray me not to kill him.

I soon found a way to convince him that I would do him no harm; and taking him up by the hand, laughed at him, and pointing to the kid which I had killed, beckoned to him to run and fetch it, which he did; and while he was wondering, and looking to see how the creature was killed, I loaded my gun again. By and by, I saw a great fowl, like a hawk, sitting upon a tree, within shot; so to let Friday understand a little what I would do, I called him to me again, pointed at the fowl, which was indeed a parrot, though I thought it had been a hawk; I say, pointing to the parrot, and to my gun, and to the ground under the parrot, to let him see I would make it fall, I made him understand that I would shoot and kill that bird; accordingly I fired and bade him look, and immediately he saw the parrot fall. He stood like one frightened again, notwithstanding all I had said to him; and I found he was the more amazed, because he did not see me put anything into the gun, but thought that there must be some wonderful fund of death and destruction in that thing, able to kill man, beast, or bird, or anything near or far off; and the astonishment this created in him was such, as could not wear off for a long time; and I believe, if I would have let him, he would have worshipped me and my gun. As for the gun itself, he would not so much as touch it for several days after; but he would speak to it, and talk to it, as if it had answered him, when he was by himself; which, as I afterwards learned of him, was to desire it not to kill him. Well, after his astonishment was a little over at this, I pointed to him to run and fetch the bird I had shot, which he did, but stayed some time; for the parrot not being quite dead, had fluttered away a good distance from the place where she fell: however, he found her, took her up, and brought her to me; and as I had perceived his ignorance about the gun before, I took this advantage to charge the gun again, and not to let him see me do it, that I might be ready for any other mark that might present; but nothing more offered at that time; so I brought home the kid, and the same evening I took the skin off, and cut it out as well as I could; and having a pot fit for that purpose I boiled or stewed some of the flesh, and made some very good broth. After I had begun to eat some, I gave some to my man, who seemed very glad of it, and liked it very well: but that which was strangest to him was to see me eat salt with it. He made a sign to me that the salt was not good to eat; and putting a little into his mouth, he seemed to nauseate it, and would spit and splutter at it, washing his mouth with fresh water after it: on the other hand, I took some meat into my mouth without salt, and I pretended to spit and splutter for want of salt, as fast as he had done at the salt; but it would not do; he would never care for salt with his meat or in his broth; at least, not for a great while, and then but very little.

Having thus fed him with boiled meat and broth, I was resolved to feast him the next day with roasting a piece of the kid; this I did by hanging it before the fire on a string, as I had seen many people do in England, setting two poles up one each side of the fire, and one across on the top, and trying the string to the cross stick, letting the meat turn continually. This Friday admired very much: but when he came to taste the flesh, he took so many ways to tell me how well he liked it, that I could not but understand him; and at last he told me, as well as he could, that he would never eat man's flesh any more, which I was very glad to hear.

The next day I set him to work to beating some corn out, and sifting it, in the manner I used to do, as I observed before; and he soon understood how to do it as well as I, especially after he had seen what the meaning of it was, and that it was to make bread of it: for after that I let him see me make my bread, and bake it too; and in a little time Friday was able to do all the work for me, as well as I could do it myself.

I began now to consider, that having two mouths to feed instead of one, I must provide more ground for my harvest, and plant a larger quantity of corn than I used to do; so I marked out a larger piece of land, and began the fence in the same manner as before, in which Friday worked not only very willingly and very hard, but did it very cheerfully: and I told him what it was for; that it was for corn to make more bread, because he was now with me, and that I might have enough for him and myself too. He appeared very sensible of that part, and let me know that he thought I had much more labour upon me on his account than I had for myself; and that he would work the harder for me if I would tell him what to do.

This was the pleasantest year of all the life I led in this place. Friday began to talk pretty well, and understand the names of almost everything I had occasion to call for, and of every place I had to send him to, and talked a great deal to me; so that, in short, I began now to have some use for my tongue again, which, indeed, I had very little occasion for before, that is to say, about speech. Besides the pleasure of talking to him, I had a singular satisfaction in the fellow himself. His simple unfeigned honesty appeared to me more and more every day, and I began really to love the creature; and, on his side, I believed he loved me more than it was possible for him ever to love anything before.

I had a mind once to try if he had any hankering inclination to his own country again; and having taught him English so well that he could answer me almost any question, I asked him "whether the nation that he belonged to never conquered in battle?" At which he smiled, and said: "Yes, yes, we always fight the better"; that is, he meant, always get the better in fight; and so we began the following discourse:

MASTER. "You always fight the better? how came you to be taken prisoner, then, Friday?"

FRIDAY. "My nation beat much, for all that."

MASTER. "How beat? If your nation beat them, how came you to be taken?"

FRIDAY. "They more maney than my nation in the place where me was; they take one, two, three, and me; my nation overbeat them in the yonder place, where me no was; there my nation take one, two, great thousand."

MASTER. "But why did not your side recover you from the hands of your enemies, then?"

FRIDAY. "They run one, two, three, and me, and make go in the canoe; my nation have no canoe that time."

MASTER. "Well, Friday, and what does your nation do with the men they take? Do they carry them away and eat them, as these did?"

FRIDAY: "Yes, my nation eat mans too; eat all up."

MASTER. "Where do they carry them?"

FRIDAY. "Go to other place, where they think."

MASTER. "Do they come hither?"

FRIDAY. "Yes, yes, they come hither; come other else place."

MASTER. "Have you been here with them?"

FRIDAY. "Yes, I have been here" (points to the N.W. side of the island, which, it seems, was their side).

By this I understood that my man Friday had formerly been among the savages who used to come on shore on the farther part of the island, on the same man-eating occasions he was now brought for; and some time after, when I took the courage to carry him to that side, being the same I formerly mentioned, he presently knew the place, and told me he was there once when they ate up twenty men, two women, and one child; he could not tell twenty in English, but he numbered them by laying so many stones in a row, and pointing to me to tell them over.

I have told this passage, because it introduces what follows; that after I had this discourse with him, I asked him how far it was from our island to the shore, and whether the canoes were not often lost. He told me there was no danger, no canoes ever lost; but that, after a little way out to sea, there was a current and wind, always one way in the morning, the other in the afternoon. This I understood to be no more than the sets of the tide, as going out or coming in; but I afterwards understood it was occasioned by the great draft and reflux of the mighty river Oroonoko, in the mouth or gulf of which river, as I found afterwards, our island lay; and that this land which I perceived to the W. and N.W. was the great island Trinidad, on the north point of the mouth of the river. I asked Friday a thousand questions about the country, the inhabitants, the sea, the coast, and what nations were near; he told me all he knew, with the greatest openness imaginable. I asked him the names of the several nations of his sort of people, but could get no other name than Caribs: from whence I easily understood, that these were Caribbese, which our maps place on the part of America which reaches from the mouth of the river Oroonoko to Guiana, and onwards to St. Martha. He told me that up a great way beyond the moon, that was, beyond the setting of the moon, which must be west from their country, there dwelt white bearded men, like me, and pointed to my great whiskers, which I mentioned before; and that they had killed much mans, that was his word: by all which I understood, he meant the Spaniards, whose cruelties in America had been spread over the whole country, and were remembered by all the nations, from father to son.

I inquired if he could tell me how I might go from this island and get among those white men; he told me, "Yes, yes, you may go in two canoe." I could not understand what he meant, or make him describe to me what he meant by two canoe; till, at last, with great difficulty, I found he meant it must be in a large boat, as big as two canoes. This part of Friday's discourse began to relish with me very well; and from this time I entertained some hopes that, one time or other, I might find an opportunity to make my escape from this place, and that this poor savage might be a means to help me.

During the long time that Friday had now been with me, and that he began to speak to me, and understand me, I was not wanting to lay a foundation of religious knowledge in his mind ; particularly I asked him, one time, who made him? The poor creature did not understand me at all, but thought I had asked him who was his father ; but I took it up by another handle, and asked him who made the sea, the ground we walked on, and the hills and woods? He told me, it was one old Benamuckee, that lived beyond all ; he could describe nothing of this great person, but that he was very old, much older, he said, than the sea or the land, than the moon or the stars. I asked him then, if this old person had made all things, why did not all things worship him? He looked very grave, and with a perfect look of innocence said : " All things say O to him." I asked him " if the people who die in his country went away anywhere? " He said, " Yes ; they all went to Benamuckee " ; then I asked him " whether those they ate up went thither too? " He said, " Yes."

From these things I began to instruct him in the knowedge of the true God ; I told him that the great Maker of all things lived up there, pointing up towards heaven ; that He governed the world by the same power and providence by which He made it; and that He was omnipotent, and could do everything for us, give everything to us, take everything from us ; and thus, by degrees, I opened his eyes. He listened with great attention, and received with pleasure the notion of Jesus Christ being sent to redeem us, and of the manner of making our prayers to God, and His being able to hear us, even in heaven. He told me one day, that if our God could hear us up beyond the sun, He must needs be a greater God than their Benamuckee, who lived but a little way off, and yet could not hear till they went up to the great mountains where he dwelt to speak to him. I asked him if ever he went thither to speak to him? He said : " No," they never went that were young men ; none went thither but the old men, whom he called their Ooowookakee : that is, as I made him explain to me, their religious, or clergy ; and that they went to say O (so he called saying prayers), and then came back and told them what Benamuckee said. I endeavoured to clear up this fraud to my man Friday; and told him that the pretence of their old men going up to the mountains to say O to their god Benamuckee was a cheat; and that their bringing word from thence what he said was much more so; that if they met with any answer, or spake with any one there, it must be an evil spirit; and then I entered into a long discourse about the devil, the original of him, his rebellion against God, his enmity to man, the reason of it, his setting himself up in the dark parts of the world to be worshipped instead of God, and as God, and the many stratagems he made use of to delude mankind to their ruin; how he had a secret access to our passions and to our affections, and to adapt his snares to our inclinations, so as to cause us even to be our own tempters, and run upon our destruction by our own choice.

I had, God knows, more sincerity than knowledge in all the methods I took for this poor creature's instruction, and must acknowledge, what I believe all that act upon the same principle will find, that in laying things open to him, I really informed and instructed myself in many things that either I did not know, or had not fully considered before, but which occurred naturally to my mind upon searching into them, for the information of this poor savage; and I had more affection in my inquiry after things upon this occasion than ever I felt before: so that, whether this poor wild wretch was the better for me or no, I had great reason to be thankful that ever he came to me; my grief sat lighter upon me; my habitation grew comfortable to me beyond measure; and when I reflected, that in this solitary life which I had been confined to, I had not only been moved to look up to Heaven myself, and to seek the hand that had brought me here, but was now to be made an instrument, under Providence, to save the life, and, for aught I knew, the soul, of a poor savage, and bring him to the true knowledge of religion, and of the Christian doctrine, that he might know Christ Jesus, in whom is life eternal; I say, when I reflected upon all these things, a secret joy ran through every part of my soul, and, I frequently rejoiced that ever I was brought to this place, which I had so often thought the most dreadful of all afflictions that could possibly have befallen me.

SECTION XXIV

ROBINSON AND FRIDAY BUILD A CANOE TO CARRY THEM TO FRIDAY'S COUNTRY—THEIR SCHEME PREVENTED BY THE ARRIVAL OF A PARTY OF SAVAGES

AFTER Friday and I became more intimately acquainted, and that he could understand almost all I said to him, and speak pretty fluently, though in broken English, to me, I acquainted him with my own history, or at least so much of it as related to my coming to this place; how I had lived here, and how long; I let him into the mystery, for such it was to him, of gunpowder and bullet, and taught him how to shoot. I gave him a knife, which he was wonderfully delighted with; and I made him a belt with a frog hanging to it, such as in England we wear hangers in; and in the frog, instead of a hanger, I gave him a hatchet, which was not only as good a weapon, in some cases, but much more useful upon other occasions.

I described to him the country of Europe, particularly England which I came from; how we lived, how we worshipped God, how we behaved to one another, and how we traded in ships to all parts of the world. I gave him an account of the wreck which I had been on board of, and showed him, as near as I could, the place where she lay; but she was all beaten in pieces before, and gone. I showed him the ruins of our boat, which we lost when we escaped, and which I could not stir with my whole strength then; but was now fallen almost to pieces. Upon seeing this boat, Friday stood musing a great while, and said nothing. I asked him what it was he studied upon? At last he says: "Me see such boat like come to place at my nation." I did not understand him a good while; but, at last, when I had examined farther into it, I understood by him, that a boat such as that had been, came on shore upon the country where he lived: that is, as he explained it, was driven thither by stress of weather. I presently imagined that some European ship must have been cast away upon their coast, and the boat might get loose, and drive ashore; but was so dull that I never once thought of men making their escape from a wreck thither, much less whence they might come; so I only inquired after a description of the boat.

Friday described the boat to me well enough; but brought me better to understand him when he added with some warmth, "We save the white mans from drown." Then I presently asked him if there were any white mans as he called them, in the boat? "Yes," he said, "the boat full of white mans." I asked him how many? He told upon his fingers seventeen. I asked him then what became of them; he told me, "They live, they dwell at my nation."

This put new thoughts into my head; for I presently imagined that these might be the men belonging to the ship that was cast away in the sight of my island, as I now called it; and who, after the ship was struck on the rock, and they saw her inevitably lost, had saved themselves in their boat, and were landed upon that wild shore among the savages. Upon this, I inquired of him more critically what was become of them; he assured me they lived still there; that they had been there about four years; that the savages let them alone, and gave them victuals to live on. I asked him how it came to pass they did not kill them and eat them; he said, "No, they make brother with them"; that is, as I understood him, a truce; and then he added. "They no eat mans but when make the war fight"; that is to say, they never eat any men but such as come to fight with them and are taken in battle.

Upon the whole, I was by this time so fixed upon my design of going over with him to the continent, that I told him we would go and make a boat as big as that, and he should go home in it. He answered not one word, but looked very grave and sad. I asked him what was the matter with him? He asked me again, "Why you angry mad with Friday? What me done?" I asked him what he meant? I told him I was not angry with him at all. "No angry?" says he, repeating the words several times; "why send Friday home away to my nation?" "Why," says I, "Friday, did not you say you wished you were there?" "Yes, yes," says he, "wish be both there; no wish Friday there, no master there." In a word he would not think of going there without me. "I go there, Friday!" says I, "what shall I do there?" He returned very quick upon me at this: "You do great deal much good," says he; "you teach wild mans be good, sober, tame mans; you tell them know God, pray God and live new life." "Alas! Friday," says I, "thou knowest not what thou sayest; I am but an ignorant man myself." "Yes, yes," says he, "you teachee me good, you teachee them good." "No, no, Friday," says I, "you shall go without me, leave me here to live by myself as I did before." He looked confused again at that word; and running to one of the hatchets which he used to wear, he takes it up hastily, and gives it to me. "What must I do with this?" says I to him. "You take kill Friday," says he. "What must I kill you for?" said I again. He returns very quick. "What you send Friday away for? Take kill Friday, no send Friday away." This he spoke so earnestly, that I saw tears stand in his eyes: in a word, I so plainly discovered the utmost affection in him to me, and a firm resolution in him, that I told him then, and often after, that I would never send him away from me, if he was willing to stay with me.

Upon the whole, as I found by all his discourse a settled affection to me, and that nothing should part him from me, so I found all the foundation of his desire to go to his own country was laid in his ardent affection to the people, and his hopes of my doing them good; a thing, which as I had no notion of myself, so I had not the least thought, or intention or desire of undertaking it. But still I found a strong inclination to my attempting an escape, as above, founded on the supposition gathered from the discourse, viz., that there were seventeen bearded men there; and, therefore, without any more delay I went to work with Friday, to find out a great tree proper to fell, and make a large periagua or canoe, to undertake the voyage. There were trees enough in the island to have built a little fleet, not of periaguas, or canoes, but even of good large vessels; but the main thing I looked at was, to get one so near the water that we might launch it when it was made, to avoid the mistake I committed at first. At last Friday pitched upon a tree; for I found he knew much better than I what kind of wood was fittest for it; nor can I tell to this day what wood to call the tree we cut down, except that it was very like the tree we call fustic, or between that and the Nicaragua wood, for it was much of the same colour and smell. Friday was for burning the hollow or cavity of the tree out, to make it for a boat, but I showed him how to cut it with tools; which, after I had showed him how to use, he did very handily; and in about a month's hard labour we finished it, and made it very handsome; especially when, with our axes, which I showed him how to handle, we cut and hewed the outside into the true shape of a boat. After this, however, it cost us near a fortnight's time to get her along, as it were inch by inch, upon great rollers into the water; but, when she was in, she would have carried twenty men with great ease.

I was near two months rigging and fitting my mast and sails; for I finished them very complete, making a small stay, and a sail or foresail to it, to assist, if we should turn to windward; and, which was more than all, I fixed a rudder to the stern of her to steer with. I was but a bungling shipwright, yet, as I knew the usefulness, and even necessity of such a thing, I applied myself with so much pains to do it, that at last I brought it to pass; though, considering the many dull contrivances I had for it that failed, I think it cost me almost as much labour as making the boat.

When the settled season began to come in, as the thought of my design returned with the fair weather, I was preparing daily for the voyage, and the first thing I did was to lay by a large quantity of provisions, being the stores for our voyage; and intended, in a week or a fortnight's time, to open the dock, and launch out our boat. I was busy one morning upon something of this kind, when I called to Friday, and bid him go to the sea-shore, and see if he could find a turtle, or tortoise, a thing we generally got once a week, for the sake of the eggs as well as the flesh. Friday had not been long gone, when he came running back and flew over my outer wall, or fence, like one that left not the ground or the steps he set his feet on; and before I had time to speak to him, he cried out to me, "O master! O master! O sorrow! O bad!" "What's the matter, Friday?" says I. "O yonder, there," says he, "one, two, three canoes; one, two, three!" By this way of speaking I concluded there were six, but on inquiry,

I found it was but three. "Well, Friday," says I, "do not be frightened!" So I heartened him up as well as I could: however, I saw the poor fellow was most terribly scared for nothing ran in his head but that they were come to look for him, and would cut him in pieces, and eat him; and the poor fellow trembled so that I scarce knew what to do with him. I comforted him as well as I could, and told him I was in as much danger as he, and that they would eat me as well as him. "But," says I, "Friday, we must resolve to fight them. Can you fight, Friday?" "Me shoot," says he, "but there come many great number." "No matter for that," said I, again, "our guns will fright them that we do not kill." So I asked him whether, if I resolved to defend him, he would defend me, and stand by me and do just as I bid him. He said, "Me die when you bid die, master." So I went and fetched a good dram of rum and gave him; for I had been so good a husband of my rum, that I had a great deal left. When he had drank it, I made him take the two fowling-pieces, which we always carried, and loaded them with large swan-shot, as big as small pistol-bullets; then I took four muskets, and loaded them with two slugs, and five small bullets each; and my two pistols I loaded with a brace of bullets each; I hung my great sword as usual, naked by my side; and gave Friday his hatchet. When I had thus prepared myself, I took my perspective glass, and went up to the side of the hill, to see what I could discover; and I found quickly by my glass, that there were one-and-twenty savages, three prisoners, and three canoes; and that their whole business seemed to be the triumphant banquet upon these three human bodies; a barbarous feast indeed, but nothing more than, as I had observed, was usual with them. I observed also, that they were landed, not where they had done when Friday made his escape, but nearer to my creek, where the shore was low, and where a thick wood came almost close down to the sea. This, with the abhorrence of the inhuman errand these wretches came about, filled me with such indignation, that I came down again to Friday, and told him that I was resolved to go down to them and kill them all; and asked him if he would stand by me. He had now got over his fright and his spirits being a little raised with the dram I had given him, he was very cheerful, and told me, as before, he would die when I bid die.

In this fit of fury I took and divided the arms which I had charged, as before, between us. I gave Friday one pistol to stick in his girdle, and three guns upon his shoulder and I took one pistol, and the other three guns myself, and in this posture we marched out. I took a small bottle of rum in my pocket, and gave Friday a large bag with more powder and bullets; and, as to orders, I charged him to keep close behind me, and not to stir, or shoot, or do anything till I bid him; and, in the meantime not to speak a word. In this posture, I fetched a compass to my right hand of near a mile, as well to get over the creek as to get into the wood, so that I might come within shot of them before I should be discovered, which I had seen, by my glass, it was easy to do.

I entered the wood and, with all possible wariness and silence, Friday following close at my heels, I marched till I came to the skirt of the wood, on the side which was next to them, only that one corner of the wood lay between me and them. Here I called softly to Friday, and showing him a great tree, which was just at the corner of the wood, I bade him go to the tree, and bring me word if he could see there plainly what they were doing. He did so, and came immediately back to me, and told me they might be plainly viewed there; that they were all about their fire, eating the flesh of one of their prisoners, and that another lay bound upon the sand, a little from them, which he said they would kill next, and which fired all the very soul within me. He told me it was not one of their nation, but one of the bearded men he told me of, that came to their country in the boat. I was filled with horror at the very naming the white bearded man; and, going to the tree, I saw plainly, by my glass a white man, who lay upon the beach of the sea, with his hands and his feet tied with flags or things like rushes and that he was a European; and had clothes on.

There was another tree and a little thicket beyond it, about fifty yards nearer to them than the place where I was, which by going a little way about, I saw I might come at undiscovered, and that then I should be within half a shot of them: so I withheld my passion, though I was indeed enraged to the highest degree ; and going back about twenty paces, I got behind some bushes, which held all the way till I came to the other tree, and then came to a little rising ground, which gave me a full view of them, at the distance of about eighty yards.

SECTION XXV

ROBINSON RELEASES A SPANIARD—FRIDAY DISCOVERS HIS FATHER—ACCOMMODATION PROVIDED FOR THESE NEW GUESTS—WHO ARE AFTERWARDS SENT TO LIBERATE THE OTHER SPANIARDS—ARRIVAL OF AN ENGLISH VESSEL

I HAD now not a moment to lose, for nineteen of the dreadful wretches sat upon the ground, all close-huddled together, and had just sent the other two to butcher the poor Christian, and bring him perhaps limb by limb to their fire ; and they were stooping down to untie the bands at his feet. I turned to Friday : "Now, Friday," said I, "do as I bid thee." Friday said he would. "Then, Friday," said I, "do exactly as you see me do ; fail in nothing." So I set down one of the muskets and the fowling-piece upon the ground, and Friday did the like by his ; and with the other musket I took my aim at the savages, bidding him to do the like ; then asking him if he was ready, he said, "Yes." "Then fire at them," said I, and the same moment I fired also.

Friday took his aim so much better than I, that on the side that he shot, he killed two of them and wounded three more ; and on my side, I killed one, and wounded two. They were, you may be sure, in dreadful consternation ; and all of them who were not hurt jumped up upon their feet, but did not immediately know which way to run, or which way to look, for they knew not from whence their destruction came. Friday kept his eyes close upon me that, as I had bid him, he might observe what I did ; so, as soon as the first shot was made, I threw down the piece, and took up the fowling-piece, and Friday did the like : he saw me cock and present, he did the same again. "Are you ready, Friday?" said I. "Yes," says he.

"Let fly, then," says I, "in the name of God!" And with that I fired again among the amazed wretches, and so did Friday; and as our pieces were now loaden with what I called swan-shot, or small pistol bullets, we found only two drop, but so many were wounded, that they ran about yelling and screaming like mad creatures, all bloody, and most of them miserably wounded, whereof three more fell quickly, after, though not quite dead.

"Now, Friday," said I, laying down the discharged pieces, and taking up the musket which was yet loaden, "follow me"; which he did with a great deal of courage; upon which I rushed out of the wood, and showed myself, and Friday close at my foot. As soon as I perceived they saw me, I shouted as loud as I could, and bade Friday do so too; and running as fast as I could, which by the way was not very fast, being loaded with arms as I was, I made directly towards the poor victim, who was, as I said, lying upon the beach, or shore, between the place where they sat and the sea. The two butchers, who were just going to work with him had left him at the surprise of our first fire, and fled in a terrible fright to the sea-side, and had jumped into a canoe, and three more of the rest made the same way. I turned to Friday and bade him step forward and fire at them; he understood me immediately, and running about forty yards, to be nearer them, he shot at them, and I thought he had killed them all, for I saw them all fall of a heap into the boat, though I saw two of them up again quickly: however, he killed two of them, and wounded the third, so that he lay down in the bottom of the boat as if he had been dead.

While my man Friday fired at them, I pulled out my knife, and cut the flags that bound the poor victim; loosing his hands and feet, I lifted him up and asked him in the Portuguese tongue, what he was. He answered in Latin, Christianus; but was so weak and faint that he could scarce stand or speak. I took my bottle out of my pocket, and gave it him, making signs that he should drink, which he did; and I gave him a piece of bread which he ate. Then I asked him what countryman he was: "Espagnole"; and being a little recovered, let me know, by all the signs he could possibly make, how much he was in my debt for his deliverance. "Signor," said I, with as much Spanish as I could make up, "we will talk afterwards but we must fight now; if you have any strength left, take this pistol and sword, and lay about you." He took them very thankfully; and no sooner had he the arms in his hands, but, as if they had put a new vigour into him, he flew upon his murderers like a fury, and had cut two of them in pieces in an instant: for the truth is the whole was a surprise to them, so the poor creatures were so much frightened with the noise of our pieces, that they fell down for mere amazement and fear, and had no more power to attempt their own escape than their flesh had to resist our shot: and that was the case of those five that Friday shot at in the boat; for as three of them fell with the hurt they had received, so the other two fell with the fright.

I kept my piece in my hand still without firing, being willing to keep my charge ready, because I had given the Spaniard my pistol and sword; so I called to Friday, and bade him run up to the tree from whence we first fired and fetch the arms which lay there that had been discharged, which he did, with great swiftness; and then giving him my musket, I sat down myself to load all the rest again, and bade them come to me when they wanted. While I was loading these pieces, there happened a fierce engagement between the Spaniard and one of the savages, who made at him with one of their great wooden swords, the same-like weapon that was to have killed him before, if I had not prevented it. The Spaniard, who was as bold and brave as could be imagined, though weak, had fought this Indian a good while, and had cut him two great wounds on his head; but the savage being a stout, lusty fellow, closing in with him, had thrown him down, being faint, and was wringing my sword out of his hand; when the Spaniard, though undermost, wisely quitted the sword, drew the pistol from his girdle, shot the savage through the body, and killed him upon the spot, before I, who was running to help him, could come near him.

Friday being now left to his liberty, pursued the flying wretches, with no weapon in his hand but his hatchet; and with that he dispatched those three, who, as I said before, were wounded at first, and fallen, and all the rest he could come up with; and the Spaniard coming to me for a gun I gave him one of the fowling-pieces, with which he pursued two of the savages, and wounded them both; but, as he was not able to run, they both got from him into the wood, where Friday pursued them, and killed one of them, but the other was too nimble for him; and though he was wounded, yet had plunged himself into the sea, and swam, with all his might, off to those who were left in the canoe, which three in the canoe with one wounded, that we know not whether he died or no, were all that escaped our hands of one-and-twenty. The account of the whole is as follows: three killed at our first shot from the tree; two killed at the next shot; two killed by Friday in the boat; two killed by Friday of those at first wounded; one killed by Friday in the wood; three killed by the Spaniard; four killed, being found dropped here and there of their wounds, or killed by Friday in his chase of them; four escaped in the boat, whereof one wounded if not dead.—Twenty-one in all.

Those who were in the canoe worked hard to get out of gun-shot, and though Friday made two or three shots at them, I did not find that he hit any of them. Friday would fain have had me take one of their canoes, and pursue them; and indeed I was very anxious about their escape, lest, carrying the news home to their people, they should come back perhaps with two or three hundred of the canoes, and devour us by mere multitude; so I consented to pursue them by sea, and running to one of their canoes, I jumped in, and bade Friday follow me; but when I was in the canoe I was surprised to find another poor creature lie there, bound hand and foot, as the Spaniard was, for the slaughter, and almost dead with fear, not knowing what was the matter; for he had not been able to look up over the side of the boat; he was tied so hard neck and heels, and had been tied so long, that he had really but little life in him.

I immediately cut the twisted flags, or rushes, which they had bound him with, and would have helped him up; but he could not stand or speak, but groaned most piteously, believing, it seems, still, that he was only unbound to be killed. When Friday came to him, I bade him speak to him, and tell him of his deliverance; and, pulling out my bottle, made him give the poor wretch a dram; which, with the news of his being delivered, revived him, and he sat up in the boat. But when Friday came to hear him speak, and look in his face, it would have moved any one to tears to have seen how Friday kissed him, embraced him, hugged him, cried, laughed, hallooed, jumped about, danced, sung; then cried again, wrung his hands, beat his own face and head; and then sang and jumped about again, like a distracted creature. It was a good while before I could make him speak to me, or tell me what was the matter; but when he came a little to himself, he told me that it was his father.

It is not easy for me to express how it moved me to see what ecstasy and filial affection had worked in this poor savage at the sight of his father, and on his being delivered from death; nor indeed can I describe half the extravagances of his affection after this; for he went into the boat, and out of the boat a great many times: when he went into him, he would sit down by him, open his breast, and hold his father's head close to his bosom for many minutes together, to nourish it; then he took his arms and ankles which were numbed and stiff with the binding, and chafed and rubbed them with his hands: and I, perceiving what the matter was, gave him some rum out of my bottle to rub them with, which did them a great deal of good.

This affair put an end to our pursuit of the canoe with the other savages, who were now almost out of sight; and it was happy for us that we did not, for it blew so hard within two hours after, and before they could have got quarter of their way, and continued blowing so hard all night, and that from the north-west, which was against them, that I could not suppose that their boat could live, or that they ever reached their own coast.

But, to return to Friday, he was so busy about his father, that I could not find in my heart to take him off for some time; but after I thought he could leave him a little, I called him to me, and he came jumping and laughing, and pleased to the highest extreme; then I asked him if he had given his father any bread. He shook his head, and said, "None; ugly dog eat all up self." I then gave him a cake of bread, out of a little pouch I carried on purpose; I also gave him a dram for himself, but he would not taste it, but carried it to his father. I had in my pocket two or three bunches of raisins, so I gave him a handful of them for his father. He had no sooner given his father these raisins, but I saw him come out of the boat, and run away, as if he had been bewitched he ran at such a rate; for he was the swiftest fellow on his feet that I ever saw; I say, he ran at such a rate, that he was out of sight, as it were, in an instant; and though I called, and hallooed out too, after him, it was all one, away he went; and in a quarter of an hour I saw him come back again, though not so fast as he went; and as he came nearer I found his pace slacker because he had something in his hand. When he came up to me, I found he had been quite home for an earthen jug, or pot, to bring his father some fresh water and that he had two more cakes or loaves of bread; the bread he gave me, but the water he carried to his father; however, as I was very thirsty too, I took a little sup of it. The water revived his father more than all the rum or spirits I had given him, for he was just fainting with thirst.

When his father had drunk, I called to him to know if there was any water left; he said "Yes," and I bade him give it to the poor Spaniard, who was in as much want of it as his father; and I sent one of the cakes that Friday brought to the Spaniard, too, who was indeed very weak, and was reposing himself upon a green place under the shade of a tree; and whose limbs were also very stiff, and very much swelled with the rude bandage he had been tied with. When I saw that, upon Friday's coming to him with the water, he sat up and drank, and took the bread, and began to eat, I went to him and gave him a handful of raisins; he looked up in my face with all the tokens of gratitude and thankfulness that could appear in any countenance; but was so weak, notwithstanding he had so exerted himself in the fight, that he could not stand up upon his feet; he tried to do it two or three times, but was really not able, his ankles were so swelled and so painful to him; so I bade him sit still, and caused Friday to rub his ankles, and bathe them with rum, as he had done his father's.

I observed the poor affectionate creature, every two minutes, or perhaps less, all the while he was here, turn his head about to see if his father was in the same place and posture as he left him sitting: and at last he found that he was not to be seen; at which he started up, and, without speaking a word, flew with that swiftness to him, that one could scarce perceive his feet to touch the ground as he went; but when he came he only found he had lain himself down to ease his limbs, so Friday came back to me presently; and then I spoke to the Spaniard to let Friday help him up, if he could, and lead him to the boat, and then he should carry him to our dwelling, where I could take care of him; but Friday, a lusty strong fellow, took the Spaniard quite up upon his back, and carried him away to the boat, and set him down softly upon the side or gunnel of the canoe, with his feet in the inside of it; and then, lifting him quite in, he set himself close to his father; and presently stepping out again, launched the boat off, and paddled it along the shore faster than I could walk, though the wind blew pretty hard too: so he brought them both safe into our creek, and leaving them in the boat, ran away to fetch the other canoe. As he passed me, I spoke to him, and asked him whither he went. He told me, "Go fetch more boat": so away he went like the wind, for sure never man or horse ran like him: and he had the other canoe in the creek almost as soon as I got to it by land; so he wafted me over, and then went to help our new guests out of the boat, which he did; but they were neither of them able to walk, so that poor Friday knew not what to do.

To remedy this, I went to work in my thought, and calling to Friday to bid them sit down on the bank while he came to me, I soon made a kind of hand-barrow to lay them on, and Friday and I carried them both up together upon it, between us. But when we got them to the outside of our wall, or fortification, we were at a worse loss than before, for it was impossible to get them over, and I was resolved not to break it down: so I set to work again; and Friday and I, in about two hours' time, made a very handsome tent, covered with old sails, and above that with boughs of trees, being in the space without our outward fence, and between that and the grove of young wood which I had planted; and here we made them two beds of such things as I had, viz., of good rice straw, with blankets laid upon it, to lie on, and another to cover them, on each bed.

My island was now peopled, and I thought myself rich in subjects; and it was a merry reflection, which I frequently made, how like a king I looked. First of all, the whole country was my own mere property, so that I had an undoubted right of dominion. Secondly, my people were perfectly subjected: I was absolutely lord and lawgiver: they all owed their lives to me, and were ready to lay down their lives, if there had been occasion for it, for me. It was remarkable, too, I had but three subjects, and they were of three different religions: my man Friday was a Protestant, his father was a Pagan and a cannibal, and the Spaniard was a Papist; however, I allowed liberty of conscience throughout my dominions.—But this is by the way.

As soon as I had secured my two weak, rescued prisoners, and given them shelter, and a place to rest them upon, I began to think of making some provision for them; and the first thing I did, I ordered Friday to take a yearling goat, betwixt a kid and a goat, out of my particular flock, to be killed; when I cut off the hinder quarter, and chopping it into small pieces, I set Friday to work to boiling and stewing, and made them a very good dish, I assure you, of flesh and broth, having put some barley and rice also into the broth; and as I cooked it without doors, for I made no fire within my inner wall, so I carried it all into the new tent, and having set a table for them, I sat down, and ate my dinner also with them, and, as well as I could, cheered them and encouraged them. Friday was my interpreter, especially to his father, and indeed, to the Spaniard too: for the Spaniard spoke the lanaguage of the savages pretty well.

After we had dined, or rather supped, I ordered Friday to take one of the canoes, and go and fetch our muskets and other fire-arms, which, for want of time, we had left upon the place of battle; and, the next day, I ordered him to go and bury the dead bodies of the savages, which lay open to the sun, and would presently be offensive. I also ordered him to bury the horrid remains of their barbarous feast, and which I could not think of doing myself; nay, I could not bear to see them, if I went that way; all which he punctually performed, and effaced the very appearance of the savages being there; so that when I went again I could scarce know where it was, otherwise than by the corner of the wood pointing to the place.

I then began to enter into a little conversation with my two new subjects; and first, I set Friday to inquire of his father what he thought of the escape of the savages in that canoe, and whether we might expect a return of them, with a power too great for us to resist. His first opinion was that the savages in the boat could never live out the storm that blew that night they went off, but must of necessity be drowned or driven south to those other shores, where they were as sure to be devoured as they were to be drowned, if they were cast away; but as to what they would do if they came safe on shore, he said he knew not; but it was his opinion, that they were so dreadfully frightened with the manner of their being attacked, the noise, and the fire, that he believed they would tell the people they were all killed by thunder and lightning, not by the hand of man; and that the two which appeared, viz., Friday and I, were two heavenly spirits, or furies, come down to destroy them, and not men with weapons. This, he said, he knew: because he heard them all cry out so, in their language, one to another; for it was impossible for them to conceive that a man could dart fire, and speak thunder, and kill at a distance, without lifting up the hand, as was done now; and this old savage was in the right; for, as I understood since, by other hands, the savages never attempted to go over to the island afterwards, they were so terrified by the accounts given by those four men (for, it seems, they did escape the sea), that they believed whoever went to that enchanted island would be destroyed by fire from the gods. This, however, I knew not; and therefore was under continual apprehensions for a good while, and kept always upon my guard, with all my army, for as there were now four of us, I would have ventured upon a hundred of them, fairly in the open field, at any time.

In a little time, however, no more canoes appearing, the fear of their coming wore off, and I began to take my former thoughts of a voyage to the main into consideration; being likewise assured by Friday's father that I might depend upon good usage from their nation, on his account, if I would go. But my thoughts were a little suspended when I had a serious discourse with the Spaniard, and when I understood that there were sixteen more of his countrymen and Portuguese, who, having been cast away, and made their escape to that side, lived there at peace, indeed, with the savages, but were very sore put to it for necessaries, and indeed for life. I asked him all the particulars of their voyage, and found they were a Spanish ship, bound from the Rio de la Plata, to the Havannah, being directed to leave their loading there, which was chiefly hides and silver, and to bring back what European goods they could meet with there; that they had five Portuguese seamen on board, whom they took out of another wreck; that five of their own men were drowned, when first the ship was lost, and that these escaped through infinite dangers and hazards, and arrived, almost starved on the cannibal coast, where they expected to have been devoured every moment. He told me they had some arms with them but they were perfectly useless, for that they had neither powder nor ball, the washing of the sea having spoiled all their powder, but a little, which they used at their first landing to provide themselves some food.

I asked him what he thought would become of them there, and if they had formed no design of making their escape. He said they had many consultations about it; but that having neither vessel, nor tools to build one, nor provisions of any kind, their councils always ended in tears and despair. I asked him how he thought they would receive a proposal from me, which might tend towards an escape; and whether if they were all here, it might not be done. I told him, with freedom, I feared mostly their treachery and ill usage of me, if I put my life in their hands, for that gratitude was no inherent virtue in the nature of man, nor did men always square their dealings by the obligations they had received, so much as they did by the advantages they expected.

He answered with a great deal of candour and ingenuousness, that their condition was so miserable, and they were so sensible of it, that he believed they would abhor the thought of using any man unkindly that should contribute to their deliverance; and that, if I pleased, he would go to them with the old man, and discourse with them about it, and return again, and bring me their answer; that he would make conditions with them upon their solemn oath, that they should be absolutely under my leading, as their commander and captain: and that they should swear, upon the holy sacraments and gospel, to be true to me, and go to such Christian country as that I should agree to, and no other, and to be directed wholly and absolutely by my orders, till they were landed safely in such country as I intended; and that he would bring a contract for them, under their hands, for that purpose.

Upon these assurances, I resolved to venture to relieve them, if possible, and to send the old savage and this Spaniard over to them to treat. But when we had got all things in readiness to go, the Spaniard himself started an objection, which had so much prudence in it, on one hand, and so much sincerity, on the other hand, that I could not but be very well satisfied in it; and, by his advice, put off the deliverance of his comrades for at least half a year. The case was thus: He had been with us now about a month, during which time I had let him see in what manner I had provided, with the assistance of Providence, for my support; and he saw evidently what stock of corn and rice I had laid up; which, though it was more than sufficient for myself, yet it was not sufficient, without good husbandry, for my family, now it was increased to four; but much less would it be sufficient if his countrymen, who were, as he said, sixteen, still alive, should come over; and least of all would it be sufficient to victual our vessel, if we should build one, for a voyage to any of the Christian colonies of America; so he told me he thought it would be more advisable to let him and the other two dig and cultivate some more land, as much as I could spare seed to sow, and that we should wait another harvest, that we might have a supply of corn for his countrymen, when they should come.

His caution was so seasonable, and his advice so good, that I could not but be very well pleased with his proposal, as well as I was satisfied with his fidelity: so we fell to digging, all four of us, as well as the wooden tools we were furnished with permitted; and in a month's time, by the end of which it was seedtime, we had got as much land cured and trimmed up as we sowed two and twenty bushels of barley on, and sixteen jars of rice; which was, in short, all the seed we had to spare; nor, indeed, did we leave ourselves barley sufficient for our own food, for the six months that we had to expect our crop; that is to say, reckoning from the time we set our seed aside for sowing; for it is not to be supposed it is six months in the ground in that country.

At the same time, I contrived to increase my little flock of tame goats as much as I could; and, for this purpose, I made Friday and the Spaniard go out one day, and myself with Friday the next day (for we took our turns), and by this means we got about twenty young kids, to breed up with the rest; for whenever we shot the dam, we saved the kids, and added them to our flock. But, above all, the season for curing the grapes coming on, I caused such a prodigious quantity to be hung up in the sun, that I believe, had we been at Alicant, where the raisins of the sun are cured, we could have filled sixty or eighty barrels: and these, with our bread was a great part of our food, and was very good living, too, I assure you, for it is exceedingly nourishing.

It was now harvest, and our crop in good order: it was not the most plentiful increase I had seen in the island, but, however, it was enough to answer our end; for from twenty-two bushels of barley we brought in and threshed out above two hundred and twenty bushels, and the like in proportion of the rice; which was store enough for our food to the next harvest though all the sixteen Spaniards had been on shore with me or if we had been ready for a voyage, it would very plentifully have victualled our ship to have carried us to any part of the world, that is to say, any part of America. When we had thus housed and secured our magazine of corn, we fell to work to make more wickerware, viz., great baskets, in which we kept it; and the Spaniard was very handy and dexterous at this part, and often blamed me that I did not make some things for defence of this kind of work; but I saw no need of it.

And now, having a full supply of food for all the guests I expected, I gave the Spaniard leave to go over to the main, to see what he could do with those he had left behind him there. I gave him a strict charge not to bring any man with him who would not first swear, in the presence of himself and the old savage, that he would no way injure, fight with, or attack the person he should find in the island, who was so kind as to send for them in order to their deliverance; but that they would stand by him, and defend him against all such attempts and wherever they went, would be entirely under and subjected to his command; and that this should be put in writing, and signed with their hands. How they were to have done this, when I knew they had neither pen nor ink, was a question which we never asked. Under these instructions, the Spaniard and the old savage, the father of Friday, went away in one of the canoes which they might be said to come in, or rather were brought in, when they came as prisoners, to be devoured by the savages. I gave each of them a musket, with a firelock on it, and about eight charges of powder and ball, charging them to be very good husbands of both, and not to use either of them but upon occasions.

This was a cheerful work, being the first measures used by me, in view of my deliverance, for now twenty-seven years and some days. I gave them provisions of bread, and of dried grapes, sufficient for themselves for many days, and sufficient for all the Spaniards for about eight days' time; and wishing them a good voyage, I saw them go; agreeing with them about a signal they should hang out at their return by which I should know them again, when they came back, at a distance, before they came on shore. They went away with a fair gale, on the day that the moon was at full, by my account in the month of October; but as for an exact reckoning of days, after I had once lost it, I could never recover it again; nor had I kept even the number of years so punctually as to be sure I was right; though, as it proved, when I afterwards examined my account, I found I had kept a true reckoning of years.

It was no less than eight days I had waited for them, when a strange and unforeseen accident intervened, of which the like had not perhaps been heard of in history. I was fast asleep in my hutch one morning, when my man Friday came running in to me, and called aloud, "Master, master, they are come, they are come!" I jumped up, and, regardless of danger, I went out as soon as I could get my clothes on, through my little grove, which, by the way, was by this time grown to a very thick wood; I say, regardless of danger, I went without my arms, which it was not my custom to do, but I was surprised, when turning my eyes to the sea, I presently saw a boat about a league and a half distance, standing in for the shore, with a shoulder-of-mutton sail, as they call it, and the wind blowing fair to bring them in: also I observed presently, that they did not come from that side which the shore lay on, but from the southernmost end of the island. Upon this, I called Friday in, and bade him lie close, for these were not the people we looked for, and that we might not know yet whether they were friends or enemies. In the next place, I went in to fetch my perspective glass to see what I could make of them; and having taken the ladder out I climbed up to the top of the hill, as I used to do when I was apprehensive of anything, and to take my view the plainer without being discovered. I had scarce set my foot upon the hill, when my eye plainly discovered a ship lying at anchor at about two leagues and a half distance from me S.S.E., but not above a league and a half from the shore. By my observation, it appeared plainly to be an English ship, and the boat appeared to be an English long-boat.

I cannot express the confusion I was in; though the joy of seeing a ship, and one that I had reason to believe was manned by my own countrymen, and, consequently, friends, was such as I cannot describe; but yet I had some secret doubts hang about me—I cannot tell from whence they came, bidding me keep upon my guard. In the first place, it occurred to me to consider what business an English ship could have in that part of the world, since it was not the way to or from any part of the world where the English had any traffic; and I knew there had been no storms to drive them in there, as in distress; and that if they were really English, it was most probable that they were here upon no good design; and that I had better continue as I was, than fall into the hands of thieves and murderers.

I had not kept myself long in this posture, but I saw the boat draw near the shore, as if they looked for a creek to thrust in at, for the convenience of landing; however, as they did not come quite far enough, they did not see the little inlet where I formerly landed my rafts, but run their boat on shore upon the beach, at about half a mile from me, which was very happy for me; for otherwise they would have landed just at my door, as I may say, and would soon have beaten me out of my castle, and perhaps have plundered me of all I had. When they were on shore, I was fully satisfied they were Englishmen, at least most of them; one or two I thought were Dutch, but it did not prove so; there were in all eleven men, whereof three I found were unarmed, and as I thought, bound; and when the first four or five of them were jumped on shore, they took those three out of the boat, as prisoners; one of the three I could perceive using the most passionate gestures of entreaty, affliction, and despair, even to a kind of extravagance; the other two, I could perceive, lifted up their hands sometimes, and appeared concerned, indeed, but not to such a degree as the first. I was perfectly confounded at the sight and knew not what the meaning of it should be. Friday called out to me in English, as well as he could, "O master! you see English mans eat prisoner as well as savage mans."

"Why, Friday," says I, "do you think they are going to eat them then?"—"Yes," says Friday, "they will eat them." "No, no," says I, "Friday; I am afraid they will murder them, indeed, but you may be sure they will not eat them."

All this while I had no thought of what the matter really was, but stood trembling with the horror of the sight, expecting every moment when the three prisoners should be killed; nay, once I saw one of the villains lift up his arm with a great cutlass, as the seamen call it, or sword, to strike one of the poor men; and I expected to see him fall at every moment; at which all the blood in my body seemed to run chill in my veins. I wished heartily now for my Spaniard, and the savage that was gone with him, or that I had any way to have come undiscovered within shot of them, that I might have rescued the three men, for I saw no fire-arms they had among them: but it fell out to my mind another way. After I had observed the outrageous usage of the three men by the insolent seamen, I observed the fellows run scattering about the island, as if they wanted to see the country. I observed that the three other men had liberty to go also where they pleased; but they sat down all three upon the ground, very pensive, and looked like men in despair. This put me in mind of the first time when I came on shore, and began to look about me: how I gave myself over for lost: how wildly I looked around me; what dreadful apprehensions I had; and how I lodged in the tree all night, for fear of being devoured by wild beasts. As I knew nothing that night of the supply I was to receive by the providential driving of the ship nearer the land by the storms and tide, by which I have been so long nourished and supported; so these three poor desolate men knew nothing how certain of deliverance and supply they were. So little do we see before us in the world, and so much reason have we to depend cheerfully upon the great Maker of the world, that He does not leave His creatures so absolutely destitute, but that, in the worst circumstances, they have always something to be thankful for, and sometimes are nearer their deliverance than they imagine; nay are even brought to their deliverance by the means by which they seem to be brought to their destruction.

SECTION XXVI

ROBINSON DISCOVERS HIMSELF TO THE ENGLISH CAPTAIN —ASSISTS HIM IN REDUCING HIS MUTINOUS CREW— WHO SUBMIT TO HIM

IT was just at the top of high water when these people came on shore; and partly while they rambled about to see what kind of a place they were in, they had carelessly stayed till the tide was spent, and the water was ebbed considerably away, leaving their boat aground. They had left two men in the boat, who, as I found afterwards, having drunk a little too much brandy, fell asleep; however, one of them waking a little sooner than the other, and finding the boat too fast aground for him to stir it, hallooed out for the rest, who were straggling about; upon which they all soon came to the boat; but it was past their strength to launch her, the boat being very heavy, and the shore on that side being a soft oozy sand, almost like a quicksand. In this condition, like true seamen, who are perhaps the least of all mankind given to forethought, they gave it over, and away they strolled about the country again: and I heard one of them say aloud to another, calling them off from the boat, "Why, let her alone, Jack, can't you? she'll float next tide," by which I was fully confirmed in the main inquiry of what countrymen they were. All this while I kept myself very close, not once daring to stir out of my castle, any farther than to my place of observation, near the top of the hill; and very glad I was to think how well it was fortified. I knew it was no less than ten hours before the boat could float again, and by that time it would be dark, and I might be at more liberty to see their motions, and to hear their discourse, if they had any. In the meantime, I fitted myself up for a battle, as before, though with more caution, knowing I had to do with another kind of enemy than I had at first. I ordered Friday also, whom I had made an excellent marksman with his gun, to load himself with arms. I took myself two fowling-pieces, and I gave him three muskets. My figure, indeed, was very fierce; I had my formidable goat's-skin coat on, with the great cap I have mentioned, a naked sword by my side, two pistols in my belt, and a gun upon each shoulder.

It was my design, as I said above, not to have made any attempt till it was dark: but about two o'clock, being the heat of the day, I found that, in short, they were all gone straggling into the woods, and as I thought, laid down to sleep. The three poor distressed men, too anxious for their condition to get any sleep, were, however, sat down under the shelter of a great tree, at about a quarter of a mile from me, and, as I thought, out of sight of any of the rest. Upon this I resolved to discover myself to them, and learn something of their condition; immediately I marched in the figure as above, my man Friday at a good distance behind me, as formidable for his arms as I, but not making quite so staring a spectre-like figure as I did. I came as near them undiscovered as I could, and then, before any of them saw me, I called aloud to them in Spanish, "What are ye, gentlemen?" They started at the noise; but were ten times more confounded when they saw me, and the uncouth figure that I made. They made no answer at all, but I thought I perceived them just going to fly from me, when I spoke to them in English: "Gentlemen," said I, "do not be surprised at me; perhaps you may have a friend near, when you did not expect it." "He must be sent directly from Heaven then," said one of them very gravely to me, and pulling off his hat at the same time to me; "for our condition is past the help of man."—"All help is from Heaven, sir," said I: "But can you put a stranger in the way how to help you? for you seem to be in some great distress. I saw you when you landed; and when you seemed to make supplication to the brutes that came with you, I saw one of them lift up his sword to kill you."

The poor man, with tears running down his face, and

trembling, looking like one astonished, returned, "Is it a real man or an angel?"—"Be in no fear about that, sir," said I; "if God had sent an angel to relieve you, he would have come better clothed, and armed after another manner than you see me: pray lay aside your fears; I am a man, an Englishman, and disposed to assist you: you see I have one servant only; we have arms and ammunition: tell us freely, can we serve you? What is your case?"—"Our case," said he, "sir, is too long to tell you, while our murderers are so near us; but, in short, sir, I was commander of that ship, my men have mutinied against me; they have been hardly prevailed on not to murder me; and at last have set me on shore in this desolate place, with these two men with me, one my mate, the other a passenger, where we expected to perish, believing the place to be uninhabited, and know not yet what to think of it."—"Where are these brutes, your enemies?" said I. "Do you know where they are gone?"—"There they lie, sir," said he, pointing to a thicket of trees; "my heart trembles for fear they have seen us, and heard you speak; if they have, they will certainly murder us all."—"Have they any fire-arms?" said I. He answered, "They had only two pieces, one of which they left in the boat."—"Well then," said I, "leave the rest to me; I see they are all asleep, it is an easy thing to kill them all: but shall we rather take them prisoners?" He told me there were two desperate villains among them, that it was scarce safe to show any mercy to; but if they were secured, he believed all the rest would return to their duty. I asked him which they were? He told me he could not at a distance distinguish them, but he would obey my orders in anything I would direct. "Well," says I, "let us retreat out of their view or hearing, lest they awake, and we will resolve further." So they willingly went back with me, till the woods covered us from them.

"Look you, sir," said I, "if I venture upon your deliverance, are you willing to make two conditions with me?" He anticipated my proposals, by telling me, that both he and the ship, if recovered, should be wholly directed and commanded by me in everything; and, if the ship was not recovered, he would live and die with me in what part of the world soever I would send him; and the two other men said the same. "Well," says I, "my conditions are but two: first, That while you stay in this island with me, you will not pretend to any authority here; and if I put arms in your hands, you will upon all occasion, give them up to me, and do no prejudice to me or mine upon this island; and, in the meantime, be governed by my orders: secondly, That if the ship is, or may be recovered, you will carry me and my man to England, passage free."

He gave me all the assurances that the invention or faith of man could devise, that he would comply with these most reasonable demands; and, besides, would owe his life to me and acknowledge it upon all occasions, as long as he lived. "Well then," said I, "here are three muskets for you, with powder and ball: tell me next what you think is proper to be done." He showed me all the testimonies of his gratitude that he was able, but offered to be wholly guided by me. I told him I thought it was hard venturing anything; but the best method I could think of was to fire upon them at once, as they lay, and if any was not killed at the first volley, and offered to submit, we might save them, and so put it wholly upon God's providence to direct the shot. He said very modestly, "that he was loth to kill them, if he could help it; but that those two were incorrigible villains, and had been the authors of all the mutiny in the ship, and if they escaped, we should be undone still; for they would go on board and bring the whole ship's company and destroy us all." "Well then," says I, "necessity legitimates my advice, for it is the only way to save our lives." However, seeing him still cautious of shedding blood, I told him they should go themselves and manage as they found convenient.

In the middle of this discourse we heard some of them awake, and soon after we saw two of them on their feet. I asked him "if either of them were the heads of the mutiny?" He said "no." "Well then," said I, "you may let them escape; and Providence seems to have awakened them on purpose to save themselves. Now," says I, "if the rest escape you, it is your fault." Animated with this, he took the musket I had given him in his hand, and a pistol in his belt, and his two comrades with him, with each a piece in his hand; the two men who were with him going first, made some noise, at which one of the seamen who was awake turned about and seeing them coming, cried out to the rest; but it was too late then, for the moment he cried out they fired; I mean the two men, the captain wisely reserving his own piece. They had so well aimed their shot at the men they knew, that one of them was killed on the spot, and the other very much wounded; but not being dead, he started up on his feet, and called eagerly for help to the others; but the captain stepping to him, told him it was too late to cry for help, he should call upon God to forgive his villainy; and with that word knocked him down with the stock of his musket, so that he never spoke more; but there were three more in the company, and one of them was also slightly wounded. By this time I was come; and when they saw their danger, and that it was in vain to resist, they begged for mercy. The captain told them he would spare their lives, if they would give him any assurance of their abhorrence of the treachery they had been guilty of, and would swear to be faithful to him in recovering the ship, and afterwards in carrying her back to Jamaica, from whence they came. They gave him all the protestations of their sincerity that could be desired, and he was willing to believe them, and spare their lives, which I was not against, only that I obliged him to keep them bound hand and foot while they were on the island.

While this was doing, I sent Friday with the captain's mate to the boat, with orders to secure her and bring away the oars and sails, which they did: and by and by three straggling men, that were (happily for them) parted from the rest, came back upon hearing the guns fired, and seeing the captain, who before was their prisoner, now their conqueror, they submitted to be bound also; and so our victory was complete.

It now remained that the captain and I should inquire into one another's circumstances; I began first, and told him my whole history, which he heard with an attention even to amazement; and particularly at the wonderful manner of my being furnished with provisions and ammunition; and, indeed, as my story is a whole collection of wonders, it affected him deeply. But when he reflected from thence upon himself, and how I seemed to have been preserved there on purpose to save his life, the tears ran down his face, and he could not speak a word more. After this communication was at an end, I carried him and his two men into my apartment, leading them in just where I came out, viz., at the top of the house, where I refreshed them with such provisions as I had, and showed them all the contrivances I had made, during my long, long inhabiting of that place.

I told him this was my castle and my residence, but that I had a seat in the country, as most princes have, whither I could retreat upon occasion, and I would show him that too another time; but at present our business was to consider how to recover the ship. He agreed with me as to that; but told me he was perfectly at a loss what measures to take, for that there were still six-and-twenty hands on board, who having entered into a cursed conspiracy, by which they had all forfeited their lives to the law, would be hardened in it now by desperation, and would carry it on, knowing that, if they were subdued, they would be brought to the gallows, as soon as they came to England, or to any of the English colonies; and that, therefore, there would be no attacking them with so small a number as we were.

I mused for some time upon what he had said, and found it was a very rational conclusion, and that, therefore, something was to be resolved on speedily, as well to draw the men on board into some snare for their surprise, as to prevent their landing upon us, and destroying us. Upon this it presently occurred to me, that in a little while the ship's crew, wondering what had become of their comrades, and of the boat, would certainly come on shore in their other boat, to look for them: and that then, perhaps, they might come armed, and be too strong for us; this he allowed to be rational. Upon this, I told him the first thing we had to do was to stave the boat, which lay upon the beach, so that they might not carry her off; and taking everything out of her, leave her so far useless as not to be fit to swim; accordingly we went on board, took the arms which were left on board out of her, and whatever else we found there.

Then we knocked a great hole in her bottom, that if they had come strong enough to master us, yet they could not carry off the boat.

While we were thus preparing our designs, and had first by main strength, heaved the boat upon the beach so high that the tide could not float her off at high-water mark, and besides, had broke a hole in her bottom too big to be quickly stopped, and were musing what we should do, we heard the ship fire a gun, and saw her make a waft with her ensign as a signal for the boat to come on board; but no boat stirred; and they fired several times, making other signals for the boat. At last when all their signals and firing proved fruitless, and they found the boat did not stir, we saw them, by the help of my glasses, hoist another boat out, and row towards the shore; and we found, as they approached, that there were no less than ten men in her, and that they had fire-arms with them.

As the ship lay almost two leagues from the shore, we had a full view of them as they came, and a plain sight even of their faces; because the tide having set them a little to the east of the other boat, they rowed up under the shore, to come to the same place where the other had landed, and where the boat lay; by this means, I say, we had a full view of them, and the captain knew the persons and characters of all the men in the boat, of whom he said there were three very honest fellows, who he was sure, were led into this conspiracy by the rest, being overpowered and frightened; but that as for the boatswain, who, it seems, was the chief officer among them, and all the rest, they were as outrageous as any of the ship's crew and were no doubt made desperate in their new enterprise; and terribly apprehensive he was that they would be too powerful for us. I smiled at him, and told him that men in our circumstances were past the operation of fear; that seeing almost every condition that could be was better than that which we were supposed to be in, we ought to expect that the conseqeunce, whether death or life, would be sure to be a deliverance.

We had, upon the first appearance of the boat's coming from the ship, considered of separating our prisoners, and we had, indeed, secured them effectually. Two of them, of whom the captain was less assured than ordinary, I sent with Friday, and one of the three delivered men, to my cave, where they were remote enough, and out of danger of being heard or discovered, or of finding their way out of the woods if they could have delivered themselves: here they left them bound, but gave them provisions; and promised them, if they continued there quietly, to give them their liberty in a day or two; but that if they attempted their escape, they should be put to death without mercy. They promised faithfully to bear their confinement with patience and were very thankful that they had such good usage as to have provisions and light left them; for Friday gave them candles (such as we made ourselves) for their comfort; and they did not know but that he stood sentinel over them at the entrance.

The other prisoners had better usage; two of them were kept pinioned, indeed, because the captain was not free to trust them: but the other two were taken into my service, upon the captain's recommendation, and upon their solemnly engaging to live and die with us; so with them and the three honest men, we were seven men well armed; and I made no doubt we should be able to deal well enough with the ten that were coming, considering that the captain had said that there were three or four honest men amongst them also. As soon as they got to the place where their other boat lay, they ran their boat into the beach, and came on shore, hauling the boat up after them, which I was glad to see; for I was afraid they would rather have left the boat at an anchor, some distance from the shore, with some hands in her to guard her, and so we should not be able to seize the boat. Being on shore, the first thing they did, they ran all to their other boat; and it was easy to see they were under a great surprise to find her stripped, as above, of all that was in her, and a great hole in her bottom. After they had mused awhile upon this, they set up two or three great shouts, hallooing with all their might, to try if they could make their companions hear, but all was to no purpose; then they came all close in a ring, and fired a volley of their small arms, which, indeed, we heard, and the echoes made the woods ring; but it was all one; those in the cave we were sure could not hear; and those in our keeping, though they heard it well enough, yet durst give no answer to them. They were so astonished at the surprise of this, that, as they told us afterwards, they resolved to go all on board again to their ship, and let them know that the men were all murdered, and the long-boat staved; accordingly, they immediately launched their boat again and got all of them on board.

The captain was terribly amazed and even confounded at this, believing they would go on board the ship again, and set sail, giving their comrades over for lost, and so he should still lose the ship, which he was in hopes we should have recovered; but he was quickly as much frightened the other way.

They had not been long put off with the boat, but we perceived them all coming on shore again; but with this new measure in their conduct, which it seems they consulted together upon, viz., to leave three men in the boat, and the rest to go on shore, and go up into the country to look for their fellows. This was a great disappointment to us, for now we were at a loss what to do; as our seizing those seven men on shore would be no advantage to us, if we let the boat escape; because they would then row away to the ship, and then the rest of them would be sure to weigh and set sail, and so our recovering the ship would be lost. However, we had no remedy but to wait and see what the issue of things might present. The seven men came on shore, and the three who remained in the boat put her off to a good distance from the shore, and came to an anchor to wait for them; so that it was impossible for us to come at them in the boat. Those who came on shore kept close together, marching towards the top of the little hill, under which my habitation lay; and we could see them plainly, though they could not perceive us. We would have been very glad if they would have come nearer to us, so that we might have fired at them, or that they would have gone farther off, that we might have come abroad. But when they were come to the brow of the hill, where they could see a great way into the valleys and woods, which lay towards the north-east part, and where the island lay lowest, they shouted and hallooed till they were weary; and not caring, it seems, to venture far from the shore, nor far from one another, they sat down together under a tree, to consider of it. Had they thought fit to have gone to sleep there, as the other part of them had done, they had done the job for us; but they were too full of apprehensions of danger to venture to go to sleep, though they could not tell what the danger was they had to fear.

The captain made a very just proposal to me upon this consultation of theirs, viz., that perhaps they would all fire a volley again, to endeavour to make their fellows hear, and that we should all sally upon them, just at the juncture when their pieces were all discharged, and they would certainly yield, and we should have them without bloodshed. I liked this proposal, provided it was done while we were near enough to come up to them before they could load their pieces again. But this even did not happen; and we lay still a long time, very irresolute what course to take. At length I told them there would be nothing done, in my opinion, till night; and then, if they did not return to the boat, perhaps we might find a way to get between them and the shore, and so might use some stratagem with them in the boat to get them on shore. We waited a great while, though very impatient for their removing; and were very uneasy, when, after long consultations, we saw them all start up, and march down towards the sea; it seems they had such dreadful apprehensions upon them of the danger of the place, that they resolved to go on board the ship again, give their companions over for lost, and so go on with their intended voyage with the ship.

As soon as I perceived them to go towards the shore, I imagined it to be, as it really was, that they had given over their search, and were for going back again; and the captain, as soon as I told him my thoughts, was ready to sink at the apprehensions of it; but I presently thought of a stratagem to fetch them back again, and which answered my end to a tittle. I ordered Friday and the captain's mate to go over the little creek westward, towards the place where the savages came on shore when Friday was rescued, and as soon as they came to a little rising ground, at about half a mile distance, I bade them halloo out, as loud as they could, and wait till they found the seamen heard them; that as soon as ever they heard the seamen answer them, they should return it again; and then keeping out of sight, take a round, always answering when the others hallooed, to draw them as far into the island and among the woods, as possible, and then wheel about again to me, by such ways as I directed them.

They were just going into the boat when Friday and the

mate hallooed: and they presently heard them, and answering, ran along the shore westward, towards the voice they heard, when they were presently stopped by the creek where the water being up, they could not get over, and called for the boat to come up and set them over; as, indeed, I expected. When they had set themselves over, I observed that the boat being gone a good way into the creek, and, as it were, in a harbour within the land, they took one of the three men out of her, to go along with them, and left only two in the boat, having fastened her to the stump of a little tree on the shore. This was what I wished for; and immediately leaving Friday and the captain's mate to their business, I took the rest with me, and crossing the creek out of their sight, we surprised the two men before they were aware: one of them lying on the shore, was between sleeping and waking, and going to start up; the captain who was foremost, ran in upon him, and knocked him down; and then called out to him in the boat to yield, or he was a dead man. There needed very few arguments to persuade a single man to yield, when he saw five men upon him, and his comrade knocked down; besides, this was, it seems, one of the three who were not so hearty in the mutiny as the rest of the crew, and therefore was easily persuaded not only to yield, but afterwards to join very sincerely with us. In the meantime, Friday and the captain's mate so well managed their business with the rest, that they drew them, by hallooing and answering from one hill to another, and from one wood to another, till they not only heartily tired them, but left them where they were very sure they could not reach back to the boat before it was dark; and, indeed, they were heartily tired themselves also, by the time they came back to us.

We had nothing now to do but to watch for them in the dark and to fall upon them, so as to make sure work with them. It was several hours after Friday came back to me before they came back to their boat; and we could hear the foremost of them, long before they came quite up, calling to those behind to come along; and could also hear them answer, and complain how lame and tired they were, and not able to come any faster, which was very welcome news to us. At length they came up to the boat; but it is impossible to express their confusion when they found the boat fast aground in the creek, the tide ebbed out, and their two men gone. I resolved to wait, to see if they did not separate; and, therefore, to make sure of them, I drew my ambuscade nearer, and ordered Friday and the captain to creep upon their hands and feet, as close to the ground as they could, that they might not be discovered, and get as near them as they could possibly, before they offered to fire.

They had not been long in that posture, when the boatswain, who was the principal ringleader of the mutiny, and had shown himself the most dejected and dispirited of all, came walking towards them, with two more of the crew; the captain was so eager at having this principal rogue so much in his power, that he could hardly have patience to let him come so near as to be sure of him, for they only heard his tongue before; but when they came nearer, the captain and Friday, starting up on their feet, let fly at them. The boatswain was killed on the spot; the next man was shot in the body, and fell just by him, though he did not die till an hour or two after; and the third ran for it. At the noise of the fire, I immediately advanced with my whole army, which was now eight men, viz., myself, generalissimo; Friday, my lieutenant-general; the captain and his two men, and the three prisoners of war, whom we had trusted with arms. We came upon them, indeed, in the dark, so that they could not see our number; and I made the man they had left in the boat, who was now one of us, to call them by name, to try if I could bring them to a parley, and so might perhaps reduce them to terms; which fell out just as we desired; for, indeed, it was easy to think, as their condition then was, they would be willing to capitulate. So he calls out as loud as he could, to one of them, "Tom Smith! Tom Smith!" Tom Smith answered immediately, "Is that Robinson?" For it seems he knew the voice. The other answered, "Ay, ay; for God's sake, Tom Smith, throw down your arms and yield, or you are all dead men this moment."—"Who must we yield to? Where are they?" says Smith again. "Here they are," says he; "here's our captain and fifty men with him, have been hunting you these two hours: the boatswain is killed, Will Fry is wounded, and I am a prisoner; and if you do not yield, you are all lost."—"Will they give us quarter then? " says Tom Smith, " and we will yield."—" I will go and ask, if you promise to yield," says Robinson: so he asked the captain; and the captain himself then calls out, " You, Smith, you know my voice; if you lay down your arms immediately, and submit you shall have your lives all but Will Atkins."

SECTION XXVII

ATKINS ENTREATS THE CAPTAIN TO SPARE HIS LIFE—THE LATTER RECOVERS HIS VESSEL FROM THE MUTINEERS —AND ROBINSON LEAVES THE ISLAND

UPON this Will Atkins cries out, " For God's sake, captain, give me quarter; what have I done? They have all been as bad as I ": which, by the way, was not true; for it seems, this Will Atkins was the first man that laid hold of the captain when they mutinied, and used him barbarously, in tying his hands, and giving him injurious language. However, the captain told him he must lay down his arms at discretion and trust to the governor's mercy; by which he meant me, for they all called me governor. In a word they all laid down their arms, and begged their lives; and I sent the man that had parleyed with them, and two more, who bound them all; and then my great army of fifty men, which particularly with those three, were in all but eight, came up and seized upon them, and upon their boat; only that I kept myself and one more out of sight for reasons of state.

Our next work was to repair the boat, and think of seizing the ship: and as for the captain, now he had leisure to parley with them, he expostulated with them upon the villainy of their practices with him, and at length upon the further wickedness of their design, and how certainly it must bring them to misery and distress in the end, and perhaps to the gallows. They all appeared very penitent and begged hard for their lives. As for that he told them that they were none of his prisoners, but the commander's of the island; that they thought they had set him on shore on a barren, uninhabited island; but it had pleased God so to direct them, that it was inhabited, and that the governor was an Englishman; that he might hang them all there, if he pleased; but as he had given them all quarter, he supposed he would send them all to England, to be dealt with there as justice required, except Atkins, whom he was commanded by the governor to advise to prepare for death, for that he would be hung in the morning.

Though all this was but a fiction of his own, yet it had the desired effect: Atkins fell upon his knees, to beg the captain to intercede with the governor for his life; and all the rest begged of him, for God's sake, that they might not be sent to England.

It now occurred to me that the time of our deliverance was come, and that it would be a most easy thing to bring these fellows in to be hearty in getting possession of the ship; so I retired in the dark from them, that they might not see what kind of a governor they had, and called the captain to me; when I called, as at a good distance, one of the men was ordered to speak again, and say to the captain, "Captain, the commander calls for you"; and presently the captain replied, "Tell his excellency I am just a-coming." This more perfectly deceived them, and they all believed that the commander was just by with his fifty men. Upon the captain's coming to me, I told him my project for seizing the ship, which he liked wonderfully well, and resolved to put it into execution the next morning. But in order to execute it with more heart, and to be secure of success, I told him we must divide the prisoners, and then he should go and take Atkins and two more of the worst of them, and send them pinioned to the cave where the others lay. This was committed to Friday and the two men who came on shore with the captain. They were conveyed to the cave as to a prison: and it was indeed a dismal place, especially to men in their condition. The others I ordered to my bower, as I called it, of which I have given a full description: and as it was fenced in and they pinioned, the place was secure enough, considering they were upon their behaviour.

To these in the morning I sent the captain, who was to enter into a parley with them; in a word, to try them, and tell me whether he thought they might be trusted or no to go on board and surprise the ship. He talked to them of the injury done him, of the condition they were brought to, and that though the governor had given them quarter for their lives as to the present action, yet that if they were sent to England, they would all be hanged in chains, to be sure: but that if they would join in so just an attempt as to recover the ship, he would have the governor's engagement for their pardon.

Any one may guess how readily such a proposal would be accepted by men in their condition; they fell down on their knees to the captain, and promised, with the deepest imprecations, that they should be faithful to him to the last drop, and that they should owe their lives to him, and would go with him all over the world: that they would own him as a father as long as they lived. "Well," says the captain, "I must go and tell the governor what you say, and see what I can do to bring him to consent to it." So he brought me an account of the temper he had found them in, and that he verily believed they would be faithful. However, that we might be very secure, I told him he should go back again and choose out those five, and tell them that they might see he did not want men, that he would take out those five to be his assistants, and that the governor would keep the other two, and the three that were sent prisoners to the castle (my cave) as hostages for the fidelity of those five; and that if they proved unfaithful in execution, the five hostages should be hanged in chains alive on the shore. This looked severe, and convinced them that the governor was in earnest: however, they had no way left them but to accept it; and it was now the business of the prisoners, as much as of the captain, to persuade the other five to do their duty.

Our strength was now thus ordered for the expedition: first the captain, his mate, and passenger; second, the two prisoners of the first gang, to whom, having their character from the captain, I had given their liberty, and trusted them with arms: third, the other two that I had kept till now in my bower, pinioned, but, on the captain's motion, had now released; fourth, these five released at last; so that these were twelve in all, besides five we kept prisoners in the cave for hostages.

When I showed myself to the two hostages, it was with the captain, who told them I was the person the governor had ordered to look after them; and that it was the governor's pleasure they should not stir anywhere but by my direction; that if they did, they would be fetched into the castle and laid in irons: so that as we never suffered them to see me as the governor, I now appeared as another person, and spoke of the governor, the garrison, the castle, and the like, upon all occasions.

The captain now had no difficulty before him, but to furnish his two boats, stop the breach of one, and man them. He made his passenger captain of one, with four of the men; and himself, his mate, and five more, went in the other; and they contrived their business very well, for they came up to the ship about midnight. As soon as they came within call of the ship, he made Robinson hail them, and tell them they had brought off the men and the boat, but that it was a long time before they had found them, and the like, holding them in a chat till they came to the ship's side; when the captain and the mate entering first with their arms, immediately knocked down the second mate and carpenter with the butt end of their muskets, being very faithfully seconded by their men; they secured all the rest that were upon the main and quarter decks, and began to fasten the hatches, to keep them down that were below; when the other boat and their men entering at the fore-chains, secured the forecastle of the ship, and the scuttle which went down into the cookroom, making three men they found there prisoners. When this was done, and all safe upon deck, the captain ordered the mate, with three men, to break into the round-house, where the new rebel captain lay, who having taken the alarm, had got up, and with two men and a boy had got fire-arms in their hands; and when the mate, with a crow, split open the door, the new captain and his men fired boldly among them, and wounded the mate with a musket-ball, which broke his arm and wounded two more of the men, but killed nobody. The mate calling for help, rushed, however, into the round-house, wounded as he was, and with his pistol shot the new captain through the head, upon which the rest yielded, and the ship was taken effectually, without any more lives lost.

As soon as the ship was thus secured, the captain ordered seven guns to be fired, which was the signal agreed upon with me to give me notice of his success, which you may be sure I was very glad to hear, having sat watching upon the shore for it till near two o'clock in the morning. Having thus heard the signal plainly, I laid me down; and it having been a day of great fatigue to me, I slept very sound, till I was something surprised with the noise of a gun; and presently starting up, I heard a man call me by the name of "Governor, Governor," and presently I knew the captain's voice; when climbing up to the top of the hill, there he stood, and pointing to the ship, he embraced me in his arms. "My dear friend and deliverer," says he, "there's your ship, for she is all yours, and so are we, and all that belongs to her." I cast my eyes to the ship, and there she rode within little more than a half mile of the shore; for they had weighed her anchor as soon as they were masters of her, and the weather being fair, had brought her to an anchor just against the mouth of the little creek; and the tide being up, the captain had brought the pinnace in near the place where I had first landed my rafts, and so landed just at my door. I was at first ready to sink down with the surprise; for I saw my deliverance, indeed, visibly put into my hands, all things easy, and a large ship just ready to carry me away whither I pleased to go. At first, for some time, I was not able to answer him one word; but as he had taken me in his arms, I held fast by him, or I should have fallen to the ground. I embraced him as my deliverer, and we rejoiced together.

When we had talked awhile, the captain told me he had brought me some little refreshment, such as the ship afforded, and such as the wretches that had been so long his masters had not plundered him of. Upon this he called aloud to the boat, and bade his men bring the things ashore that were for the governor; and, indeed, it was a present as if I had been one that was not to be carried away with them, but as if I had been to dwell upon the island still. First, he had brought me a case of bottles full of excellent cordial waters, six large bottles of Madeira wine (the bottles held two quarts each), two pounds of excellent good tobacco, twelve good pieces of the ship's beef, and six pieces of pork, with a bag of peas, and about a hundredweight of biscuits; he also brought me a box of sugar, a box of flour, a bag full of lemons, and two bottles of lime juice, and abundance of other things. But, besides these, and what was a thousand times more useful to me, he brought me six new clean shirts, six very good neckcloths, two pairs of gloves, one pair of shoes, a hat, and one pair of stockings, with a very good suit of clothes of his own, which had been worn but very little; in a word, he clothed me from head to foot. It was a very kind and agreeable present, as any one may imagine, to one in my circumstances, but never was anything in the world of that kind so unpleasant, awkward, and uneasy, as it was to me to wear such clothes at first.

After these ceremonies were past, and after all his good things were brought into my little apartment, we began to consult what was to be done with the prisoners we had; for it was worth considering whether we might venture to take them away with us or no, especially two of them, whom we knew to be incorrigible and refractory to the last degree: and the captain said he knew they were such rogues, that there was no obliging them; that if he did carry them away, it must be in irons, as malefactors, to be delivered over to justice at the first English colony he could come at; and I found that the captain himself was very anxious about it. Upon this I told him, that if he desired it, I would undertake to bring the two men he spoke of to make it their own request that he should leave them upon the island. "I should be very glad of that," says the captain, "with all my heart." "Well," says I, "I will send for them up, and talk with them for you." So I caused Friday and the two hostages, for they were now discharged, their comrades having performed their promise: I say, I caused them to go to the cave and bring up the five men, pinioned as they were, to the bower, and keep them there till I came. After some time, I came thither dressed in my new habit; and now I was called the governor again. Being all met, and the captain with me, I caused the men to be brought before me, and I told them I had got a full account of their villainous behaviour to their captain, and how they had run away with the ship, and were preparing to commit further robberies, but that Providence had ensnared them in their own ways, and that they were fallen into the pit which they had dug for others. I let them know that by my direction the ship had been seized; that she lay now in the road; and they might see by and by, that their new captain had received the reward of his villainy, and that they would see him hanging at the yard-arm: that as to them, I wanted to know what they had to say why I should not execute them as pirates, taken in the fact, as by my commission they could not doubt but I had authority so to do.

One of them answered in the name of the rest, that they had nothing to say but this, that when they were taken, the captain promised them their lives, and they humbly implored my mercy. But I told them I knew not what mercy to show them; for as for myself, I had resolved to quit the island with all my men, and had taken a passage with the captain to go to England; and as for the captain he could not carry them to England other than as prisoners, in irons, to be tried for mutiny, and running away with the ship: the consequence of which, they must needs know, would be the gallows; so that I could not tell what was best for them, unless they had a mind to take their fate in the island; if they desired that, as I had liberty to leave the island, I had some inclination to give them their lives, if they thought they could shift on shore. They seemed very thankful for it, and said they would much rather venture to stay there than be carried to England to be hanged; so I left it on that issue.

When they had all declared their willingness to stay, I then told them I would let them into the story of my living there, and put them into the way of making it easy to them; accordingly, I gave them the whole story of the place, and of my coming to it; showed them my fortifications, the way I made my bread, planted my corn, cured my grapes; and, in a word, all that was necessary to make them easy. I told them the story also of the seventeen Spaniards that were to be expected, for whom I left a letter, and made them promise to treat them in common with themselves. Here it may be noted that the captain had ink on board, who was greatly surprised that I never hit upon a way of making ink of charcoal and water, or of something else, as I had done things much more difficult.

However, the captain seemed to make some difficulty of it, as if he durst not leave them there. Upon this I seemed a little angry with the captain, and told him that they were my prisoners, not his; and seeing that I had offered them so much favour, I would be as good as my word: and that if he did not think fit to consent to it, I would set them at liberty, as I found them; and if he did not like it he might take them again, if he could catch them. Upon this they appeared very thankful, and I accordingly set them at liberty, and bade them retire into the woods to the place whence they came, and I would leave them some fire-arms, some ammunition, and some directions how they should live very well, if they thought fit. Upon this I prepared to go on board the ship; but told the captain I would stay that night to prepare my things, and desired him to go on board, in the meantime, and keep all right in the ship, and send the boat on shore next day for me; ordering him, at all events to cause the new captain, who was killed, to be hanged at the yard-arm, that these men might see him.

I left them my fire-arms, viz., five muskets, three fowling-pieces, and three swords. I had above a barrel and a half of powder left; for after the first year or two I used but little, and wasted none. I gave them a description of the way I managed the goats, and directions to milk and fatten them, and to make both butter and cheese; in a word, I gave them every part of my own story, and told them I should prevail with the captain to leave them two barrels of gunpowder more, and some garden seeds, which I told them I would have been very glad of; also I gave them the bag of peas which the captain had brought me to eat, and bade them be sure to sow and increase them.

Having done all this, I left them the next day, and went on board the ship. We prepared immediately to sail, but did not weigh that night. The next morning early, two of the five men came swimming to the ship's side, and making a most lamentable complaint of the other three, begged to be taken into the ship, for God's sake, for they should be murdered, and begged to the captain to take them on board, though he hanged them immediately. Upon this the captain pretended to have no power without me; but after some difficulty, and after their solemn promises of amendment, they were taken on board and were some time after soundly whipped and pickled: after which they proved very honest and quiet fellows.

Some time after this, the boat was ordered on shore, the tide being up, with the things promised to the men; to which the captain, at my intercession, caused their chests and clothes to be added, which they took, and were very thankful for. I also encouraged them by telling them that if it lay in my power to send any vessel to take them in, I would not forget them.

When I took leave of this island I carried on board, for reliques, the great goat-skin cap I had made, my umbrella, and one of my parrots; also I forgot not to take the money I formerly mentioned, which had lain by me so long useless that it had grown rusty or tarnished, and could hardly pass for silver, till it had been a little rubbed and handled; as also the money I found in the wreck of the Spanish ship. And thus I left the island, the 19th of December, as I found by the ship's account, in the year 1686, after I had been upon it eight-and-twenty years, two months, and nineteen days, being delivered from this second captivity the same day of the month that I first made my escape in the long-boat from among the Moors of Sallee. In this vessel, after a long voyage, I arrived in England the 11th of June, in the year 1687, having been thirty-five years absent.

SECTION XXVIII

ROBINSON GOES TO LISBON, WHERE HE FINDS THE PORTUGUESE CAPTAIN, WHO RENDERS HIM AN ACCOUNT OF HIS PROPERTY IN THE BRAZILS—SETS OUT ON HIS RETURN TO ENGLAND BY LAND

WHEN I came to England, I was as perfect a stranger to all the world as if I had never been known there. My benefactor and faithful steward, whom I left my money in trust with, was alive, but had had great misfortunes in the world; was become a widow the second time, and very low in the world. I made her very easy as to what she owed me, assuring her I would give her no trouble; but on the contrary, in gratitude for former care and faithfulness to me, I relieved her as well as my little stock would afford;

which at the time, would allow me to do but little for her; but I assured her I would never forget her former kindness to me; nor did I forget her when I had sufficient to help her, as shall be observed in its proper place. I went down afterwards into Yorkshire: but my father and mother were dead, and all the family extinct, except that I found two sisters and two of the children of one of my brothers, and as I had been long ago given over for dead, there had been no provision made for me: so that in a word, I found nothing to relieve me or assist me; and that the little money I had would not do much for me as to settling in the world.

I met with one piece of gratitude, indeed, which I did not expect; and this was, that the master of the ship whom I so happily delivered, and by the same means saved the ship and cargo, having given a very handsome account to the owners of the manner how I had saved the lives of the men and the ship, they invited me to meet them, and some other merchants concerned, and all together made me a very handsome compliment upon the subject, and a present of almost two hundred pounds sterling.

But after making several reflections upon the circumstances of my life, and how little way this would go towards settling me in the world, I resolved to go to Lisbon, and see if I might not come by some information of the state of my plantation in the Brazils, and of what was become of my partner, who, I had reason to suppose, had some years past given me over for dead. With this view I took shipping for Lisbon, where I arrived in April following; my man Friday accompanying me very honestly in all these ramblings, and proving a most faithful servant upon all occasions. When I came to Lisbon, I found out, by inquiry, and to my particular satisfaction, my old friend the captain of the ship who first took me up at sea off the shore of Africa. He was now grown old, and had left off going to sea, having put his son, who was far from a young man, into his ship, and who still used the Brazil trade.

After some passionate expressions of the old acquaintance between us, I inquired, you may be sure, after my plantation and my partner. The old man told me he had not been in the Brazils for about nine years; but that he could assure me that when he came away my partner was living; but the trustees, whom I had joined with him to take cognizance of my part, were both dead; that, however, he believed I would have a very good account of the improvement of the plantation; for that upon the general belief of my being cast away and drowned, my trustees had given in the account of the produce of my part of the plantation to the procurator-fiscal, who had appropriated it, in case I never came to claim it, one-third to the king, and two-thirds to the monastery of St. Augustine, to be expended for the benefit of the poor, and for the conversion of the Indians to the Catholic faith; but that if I appeared, or any one for me, to claim the inheritance, it would be restored; only that the improvement or annual production, being distributed to charitable uses, could not be restored: but he assured me that the steward of the king's revenue from lands, and the proviedore, or steward of the monastery, had taken great care all along that the incumbent, that is to say, my partner, gave every year a faithful account of the produce, of which they had duly received my moiety. He told me he could not tell exactly to what degree the plantation was improved, but this he knew, that my partner was grown exceeding rich upon the enjoying his part of it; that as to my being restored to a quiet possession of it, there was no question to be made of that, my partner being alive to witness my title, and my name being also enrolled in the register of the country; also he told me, that the survivors of my two trustees were very fair honest people, and very wealthy: and he believed I would not only have their assistance for putting me in possession, but would find a very considerable sum of money in their hands for my account, being the produce of the farm while their fathers held the trust, and before it was given up, as above; which, as he remembered, was for about twelve years.

I showed myself a little concerned and uneasy at this account, and inquired of the old captain how it came to pass that the trustees should thus dispose of my effects, when he knew that I had made my will, and had made him, the Portuguese captain, my universal heir, etc.

He told me that was true; but that as there was no proof of my being dead, he could not act as executor, until some certain account should come of my death; and, besides, he was not willing to intermeddle with a thing so remote: that it was true he had registered my will, and put in his claim; and could he have given any account of my being dead or alive, he would have acted by procuration, and taken possession of the ingenio (so they called the sugar-house), and have given his son, who was now at the Brazils, orders to do it. "But," says the old man, "I have one piece of news to tell you, which, perhaps, may not be so acceptable to you as the rest; and that is believing you were lost, and all the world believing so also, your partner and trustees did offer to account with me, in your name, for six or eight of the first year's profits, which I received." There being at that time great disbursements for increasing the works, building an ingenio, and buying slaves, it did not amount to near so much as afterwards it produced: "However," says the old man, "I shall give you a true account of what I have received in all, and how I have disposed of it."

After a few days' further conference with this ancient friend, he brought me an account of the first six years' income of my plantation, signed by my partner and the merchant trustees, being always delivered in goods, viz., tobacco in roll, and sugar in chests, besides rum, molasses, etc., which is the consequence of a sugar-work; and I found, by this account, that every year the income considerably increased; but, as above, the disbursements being large, the sum at first was small; however, the old man let me see that he was debtor to me four hundred and seventy moidores of gold, besides sixty chests of sugar and fifteen double rolls of tobacco, which were lost in his ship; he having been shipwrecked coming home to Lisbon about eleven years after my leaving the place. The good man then began to complain of his misfortunes, and how he had been obliged to make use of my money to recover his losses, and buy him a share in a new ship. "However, my old friend," says he, "you shall not want a supply in your necessity; and as soon as my son returns, you shall be fully satisfied." Upon this, he pulls out an old pouch, and gives me one hundred and sixty Portugal moidores in gold; and taking the writings of his title to the ship, which his son was gone to the Brazils in, of which he was a quarter part owner, and his son another, he puts them both into my hands, for security of the rest.

I was too much moved with the honesty and kindness of the poor man to be able to bear this; and remembering what he had done for me, how he had taken me up at sea, and how generously he had used me on all occasions, and particularly how sincere a friend he was now to me, I could hardly refrain weeping at what he said to me; therefore I asked him if his circumstances admitted him to spare so much money at that time, and if it would not straiten him? He told me he could not say but it might straiten him a little; but, however, it was my money, and I might want it more than he.

Everything the good man said was full of affection, and I could hardly refrain from tears while he spoke; in short, I took one hundred of the moidores, and called for a pen and ink to give him a receipt for them: then I returned him the rest, and told him if ever I had possession of the plantation I would return the other to him also (as, indeed, I afterwards did); and that as to the bill of sale of his part in his son's ship, I would not take it by any means: but that if I wanted the money, I found he was honest enough to pay me; and if I did not, but came to receive what he gave me reason to expect, I would never have a penny more from him.

When this was past, the old man asked me if he should put me into the method to make my claim to my plantation? I told him I thought to go over to it myself. He said I might do so, if I pleased; but that if I did not, there were ways enough to secure my right, and immediately to appropriate the profits to my use: and as there were ships in the river of Lisbon just ready to go away to Brazil he made me enter my name in a public register, with his affidavit, affirming, upon oath, that I was alive, and that I was the same person who took up the land for the planting the said plantation at first. This being regularly attested by a notary, and a procuration affixed, he directed me to send it, with a letter of his writing, to a merchant of his acquaintance at the place; and then proposed my staying with him till an account came of the return.

Never was anything more honourable than the proceedings upon this procuration; for in less than seven months I received a large packet from the survivors of my trustees, the merchants, for whose account I went to sea, in which were the following particular letters and papers enclosed :

First, There was the account-current of the produce of my farm or plantation, from the year when their fathers had balanced with my old Portugal captain, being for six years : the balance appeared to be one thousand one hundred and seventy-four moidores in my favour.

Secondly, There was an account of four years more, while they kept the effects in their hands, before the government claimed the administration, as being the effects of a person not to be found, which they called civil death; and the balance of this amounted to nineteen thousand four hundred and forty-six crusadoes, being about three thousand two hundred and forty moidores.

Thirdly, There was the prior of Augustine's account, who had received the profits for above fourteen years; but not being to account for what was disposed of by the hospital, very honestly declared he had eight hundred and seventy-two moidores not distributed, which he acknowledged to my account; as to the king's part that refunded nothing.

There was a letter of my partner's congratulating me affectionately upon my being alive, giving me an account how the estate had improved, and what it produced a year; with a particular of the number of squares or acres that it contained, how planted, how many slaves there were upon it, and making two and twenty crosses for blessings, told me he had said so many *Ave Marias* to thank the blessed Virgin that I was alive; inviting me very passionately to come over and take possession of my own; and, in the meantime, to give him orders to whom he should deliver my effects, if I did not come myself : concluding with a hearty tender of his friendship, and that of his family ; and sent me, as a present, seven fine leopards' skins, which he had, it seems, received from Africa, by some other ship he had sent thither, and who, it seems, had made a better voyage than I. He sent me also five chests of excellent sweetmeats, and a hundred pieces of gold uncoined, not quite so large as moidores. By the same fleet my two merchant trustees shipped me one thousand two hundred chests of sugar, eight hundred rolls of tobacco, and the rest of the whole account in gold.

I might well say now, indeed, the latter end of the job

was better than the beginning. It is impossible to express the flutterings of my very heart, when I found all my wealth about me; for as the Brazil ships came all in fleets, the same ships which brought my letters brought my goods; and the effects were safe in the river before the letters came to my hand.

I was now master, all of a sudden, of above five thousand pounds sterling in money, and had an estate, as I might well call it, in the Brazils, of above a thousand pounds a year, as sure as an estate of lands in England; and, in a word, I was in a condition which I scarce knew how to understand, or how to compose myself for the enjoyment of it. The first thing I did was to recompense my original benefactor, my good old captain, who had been first charitable to me in my distress, kind to me in my beginning, and honest to me at the end. I showed him all that was sent to me; I told him that next to the providence of Heaven, which disposed all things, it was owing to him; and that it now lay on me to reward him, which I would do a hundredfold: so I first returned the hundred moidores I had received of him; then I sent for a notary, and caused him to draw up a general release or discharge from the four hundred and seventy moidores, which he had acknowledged he owed me, in the fullest and firmest manner possible. After which I caused a procuration to be drawn, empowering him to be my receiver of the annual profits of my plantation, and appointing my partner to account with him, and make the returns by the usual fleets to him in my name: and a clause in the end, being a grant of one hundred moidores a year to him during his life, out of the effects, and fifty moidores a year to his son after him, for his life; and thus I requited my old man.

Having settled my affairs, sold my cargo, and turned all my effects into good bills of exchange, my next difficulty was, which way to go to England; I had been accustomed enough to the sea, and yet I had a strange aversion to go to England by sea at that time; and though I could give no reason for it, yet the difficulty increased upon me so much, that though I had once shipped my baggage, in order to go, yet I altered my mind, and that not once, but two or three times.

Having thus been harassed in my thoughts, my old

pilot to whom I communicated everything, pressed me earnestly not to go by sea, but either to go by land to the Groyne (Corunna), and cross over the Bay of Biscay to Rochelle, from whence it was but an easy and safe journey by land to Paris, and so to Calais and Dover, to go up to Madrid, and so all the way by land through France. In a word, I was so prepossessed against my going by sea at all, except from Calais to Dover, that I resolved to travel all the way by land; which, as I was not in haste, and did not value the charge, was by much the pleasanter way: and to make it more so, my old captain brought an English gentleman, the son of a merchant in Lisbon, who was willing to travel with me; after which we picked up two more English merchants also, and two young Portuguese gentlemen, the last going to Paris only; so that in all there were six of us, and five servants; the two merchants and the two Portuguese contenting themselves with one servant between two, to save the charge; and as for me, I got an English sailor to travel with me as a servant, besides my man Friday, who was too much a stranger to be capable of supplying the place of a servant on the road.

In this manner I set out from Lisbon; and our company being very well mounted and armed, we made a little troop, whereof they did me the honour to call me captain, as well because I was the oldest man, as because I had two servants, and, indeed, was the original of the whole journey.

As I have troubled you with none of my sea journals, so I shall trouble you now with none of my land journal; but some adventures that happened to us in this tedious and difficult journey I must not omit.

When we came to Madrid, we being all of us strangers to Spain, were willing to stay some time to see the Court of Spain, and to see what was worth observing; but it being the latter part of the summer, we hastened away, and set out from Madrid about the middle of October; but when we came to the edge of Navarre, we were alarmed at several towns on the way, with an account that so much snow was fallen on the French side of the mountains, that several travellers were obliged to come back to Pampeluna, after having attempted, at an extreme hazard, to pass on.

When we came to Pampeluna itself, we found it so, indeed; and to me, that had always been used to a hot climate, and to countries where I could scarce bear any clothes on, the cold was insufferable; nor, indeed, was it more strange than surprising, to come but ten days before out of Old Castile, where the weather was not only warm but very hot, and immediately to feel a wind from the Pyrenean mountains, so very keen, so severely cold, as to be intolerable, and to endanger the benumbing and perishing of our fingers and toes.

We stayed no less than twenty days at Pampeluna; when seeing the winter coming on, and no likelihood of its being better, for it was the severest winter all over Europe that had been known in the memory of man, I proposed that we should all go away to Fontarabia and there take shipping for Bordeaux, which was a very little voyage. But while I was considering this, there came in four French gentlemen, who having been stopped on the French side of the passes, as we were on the Spanish, had found out a guide, who, traversing the country near the head of Languedoc, had brought them over the mountains by such ways, that they were not much incommoded with the snow; for where they met with snow in any quantity, they said it was frozen hard enough to bear them and their horses. We sent for this guide, who told us he would undertake to carry us the same way with no hazard from the snow, provided we were armed sufficient to protect ourselves from wild beasts; for, he said, upon these great snows it was frequent for some wolves to show themselves at the foot of the mountains, being made ravenous for want of food, the ground being covered with snow. We told him we were well enough prepared for such creatures as they were if he would ensure us from a kind of two-legged wolves, which, we were told, we were in most danger from, especially on the French side of the mountains. He satisfied us that there was no danger of that kind in the way we were to go; so we readily agreed to follow him, as did also twelve other gentlemen, with their servants, some French, some Spanish, who, as I said, had attempted to go, and were obliged to come back again.

Accordingly, we set out from Pampeluna, with our guide, on the 15th of November; and, indeed, I was surprised, when, instead of going forward, he came directly back with us on the same road that we came from Madrid, about twenty miles; when having passed two rivers, and come into the plain country we found ourselves in a warm climate again, where the country was pleasant, and no snow to be seen; but on a sudden turning to his left, he approached the mountains another way: and though it is true the hills and precipices looked dreadful, yet he made so many tours, such meanders, and led us by such winding ways, that we insensibly passed the height of the mountains without being much encumbered with the snow; and, all on a sudden, he showed us the pleasant fruitful provinces of Languedoc and Gascony, all green and flourishing, though, indeed, at a great distance, and we had some rough way to pass still.

We were a little uneasy, however, when we found it snowed one whole day and a night so fast, that we could not travel; but he bid us be easy, we should soon be past it all; we found, indeed, that we began to descend every day, and to come more north than before; and so, depending upon our guide, we went on.

SECTION XXIX

FRIDAY'S ENCOUNTER WITH A BEAR—ROBINSON AND HIS FELLOW TRAVELLERS ATTACKED BY A FLOCK OF WOLVES —HIS ARRANGEMENT OF HIS AFFAIRS, AND MARRIAGE AFTER HIS RETURN TO ENGLAND

It was about two hours before night, when our guide being some way before us, and not just in sight, out rushed three monstrous wolves, and after them a bear, out of a hollow way adjoining to a thick wood; two of the wolves, made at the guide, and had he been far before us, he would have been devoured before we could have helped him; one of them fastened upon his horse, and the other attacked the man with that violence, that he had not time, or presence of mind enough to draw his pistol, but hallooed and cried out to us most lustily. My man Friday being next to me, I bade him ride up, and see what was the matter.

As soon as Friday came in sight of the man, he hallooed out as loud as the other, "O master! O master!" but like a bold fellow, rode directly up to the poor man, and with his pistol shot the wolf in the head that attacked him.

My man Friday had delivered our guide, and when we came up to him, he was helping him off from his horse, for the man was both hurt and frightened, when, on a sudden, we espied the bear come out of the wood, and a vast, monstrous one it was, the biggest by far that I ever saw. We were all a little surprised when we saw him; but when Friday saw him, it was easy to see joy and courage in the fellow's countenance; "O, O, O!" says Friday, three times, pointing to him; "O, master! you give me te leave, me shakee te hand with him; me makee you good laugh."

I was surprised to see the fellow so well pleased; "You fool," says I, "he will eat you up." "Eatee me up! eatee me up!" says Friday, twice over again: "me eatee him up, me makee you good laugh." So down he sits, and gets off his boots in a moment, and puts on a pair of pumps (as we call the flat shoes they wear, and which he had in his pocket), gives my other servant his horse, and with his gun, away he flew, swift like the wind.

The bear was walking softly on and offered to meddle with nobody, till Friday, who had, as we say, the heels of the bear, came up, and takes a great stone and throws it at him, and hit him just on the head, but did him no more harm than if he had thrown it against a wall; but it answered Friday's end, for the rogue was so void of fear, that he did it purely to make the bear follow him, and show us some laugh as he called it. As soon as the bear felt the blow, and saw him, he turns about, and comes after him, taking long strides and shuffling on at a strange rate, such as would put a horse to a middling gallop; away runs Friday, and takes his course as if he runs towards us, he turned on a sudden, on one side of us, and seeing a great oak tree fit for his purpose, he beckoned to us to follow; and doubling his pace, he gets nimbly up the tree, laying his gun down upon the ground, at about five or six yards from the bottom of the tree. The bear soon came to the tree, and we followed at a distance; the first thing he did, he stopped at the gun, smelt it, but let it lie, and up he scrambles into the tree, climbing like a cat, though so monstrous heavy. I was amazed at the folly, as I thought it, of my man, and could not for my life see anything to laugh at yet, till seeing the bear get up the tree, we all rode near to him.

When we came to the tree, there was Friday got out to the small end of a large branch, and the bear got about half-way to him. As soon as the bear got out to that part where the limb of the tree was weaker: "Ha!" says he to us, "now you see me teachee the bear dance"; so he falls a jumping and shaking the bough, at which the bear began to totter, but stood still, and began to look behind him, to see how he should get back; then, indeed, we did laugh heartily. We thought now it was a good time to knock him on the head, and called to Friday to stand still, and we would shoot the bear; but he cried out earnestly: "O pray! O pray! no shoot, me shoot by and then"; he would have said by and by. However, he goes out to the smaller end of the bough, where it would bend with his weight, and gently lets himself down with it, sliding down the bough, till he came near enough to jump down on his feet, and away he runs to his gun, takes it up, and stands still. "Well," said I to him, "Friday, what will you do now? Why don't you shoot him?" "No shoot," says Friday, "not yet; me to shoot now, me to kill; me stay, give you one more laugh"; and, indeed, so he did, as you will see presently; for when the bear saw his enemy gone, he comes back from the bough where he stood, but did it mighty cautiously, looking behind him every step, and coming backward till he got into the body of the tree; then with the same hinder-end foremost, he came down the tree, grasping it with his claws and moving one foot at a time, very leisurely. At this juncture, and just before he could set his hind-foot on the ground, Friday stepped up close to him, clapped the muzzle of the piece into his ear, and shot him dead. Then the rogue turned about, to see if we did not laugh; and when he saw we were pleased, by our looks, he falls a-laughing himself very loud. "So we kill bear in my country," says Friday. "So you kill them?" says I, "why you have no guns." "No," says he, "no gun, but shoot great much long arrow." This was a good diversion to us; but we were still in a wild place, and our guide very much hurt, and what to do we hardly knew; the howling wolves ran much in my head, and, indeed, except the noise I once heard on the shore of Africa, of which I have said something already, I never heard anything that filled me with so much horror.

These things, and the approach of night, called us off, or else, as Friday would have had us, we should certainly have taken the skin of this monstrous creature off, which was worth saving; but we had near three leagues to go, and our guide hastened us, so we left him, and went forward on our journey.

We were not gone half over the plain, when we began to hear the wolves howl in the wood on our left in a frightful manner, and presently after, we saw about a hundred coming on directly towards us, all in a body, and most of them in a line, as regularly as an army drawn up by an experienced officer. I scarce knew in what manner to receive them, but found to draw ourselves in a close line was the only way; so we formed in a moment; but that we might not have too much interval, I ordered that only every other man should fire, and that those others who had not fired should stand ready to give them a second volley immediately, if they continued to advance upon us; and then that those who had fired at first, should not pretend to load their fuses again, but stand ready every one with a pistol, for we were all armed with a fuse and a pair of pistols each man; so we were, by this method, able to fire six volleys, half of us at a time. However, at present we had no necessity, for upon firing the first volley, the enemy made a full stop, being terrified as well with the noise as with the fire; four of them, being shot in the head dropped; several others were wounded and went bleeding off, as we could see by the snow. I found they stopped, but did not immediately retreat; whereupon, remembering that I had been told that the fiercest creatures were terrified by the voice of a man, I caused all the company to halloo as loud as we could, and I found the notion not altogether mistaken; for upon our shout, they began to retire and turn about.

The night was coming on, and the light began to be dusky, which made it worse on our side; when, and on a sudden we perceived two or three troops of wolves, one on our left, one behind us, and one in our front, so that we seemed surrounded by them. However, as they did not fall upon us, we kept our way forward, as fast as we could make our horses go, which, the way being very rough, was only a good hard trot. In this manner we came in view of the entrance of the wood, through which we were to pass, at the farther side of the plain; but we were greatly surprised, when, coming nearer the lane or pass, we saw a confused number of wolves standing just at the entrance. On a sudden, at another opening of a wood, we heard the noise of a gun and looking that way, out rushed a horse, with a saddle and bridle on him, flying like the wind, and sixteen or seventeen wolves after him full speed.

But here we had a most horrible sight; for riding up to the entrance where the horse came out, we found the carcases of another horse and of two men, devoured by the ravenous creatures; and one of the men was no doubt the same whom we heard fire the gun, for there lay a gun just by him fired off; but as to the man, his head and the upper part of his body were eaten up. This filled us with horror, and we knew not what course to take; but the creatures resolved us soon, for they gathered about us presently, in hopes of prey; and I verily believe there were three hundred of them. It happened very much to our advantage, that at the entrance into the wood, but a little way from it, there lay some large timber trees, which had been cut down the summer before, and I suppose lay there for carriage. I drew my little troop in among those trees, and placing ourselves in a line behind one long tree, I advised them all to alight, and keeping that tree before us for a breastwork, to stand in a triangle or three fronts enclosing our horses in the centre. We did so, and it was well we did; for never was a more furious charge than the creatures made. I ordered our men to fire as before, every other man; and they took aim so sure that they killed several of the wolves at the first volley; but there was a necessity to keep a continual firing, for they came on like devils, those behind pushing on those before.

When we had fired a second volley of our fuses, we thought they stopped a little; and I hoped they would have gone off; but it was only a moment, for others came forward again; so we fired two volleys of our pistols, and I believe in these four firings we had killed seventeen or eighteen of them, and lamed twice as many, yet they came on again. I was loth to spend our shot too hastily; so I called my servant, not my man Friday, and giving him a horn of powder, I bade him lay a train all along the piece of timber, and let it be a large train. He did so; and had but just time to get away, when the wolves came up to it, and some got upon it, when I, snapping an uncharged pistol close to the powder, and set it on fire; those that were upon the timber were so scorched with it that they drew back a little; upon which I ordered our last pistols to be fired off in one volley, and after that we gave a shout: upon this the wolves turned tail, and we sallied immediately upon near twenty lame ones, that we found struggling on the ground, and fell a cutting them with our swords, which answered our expectation; for the crying and howling they made was better understood by their fellows; so that they all fled and left us.

In about an hour more we came to the town where we were to lodge.

The next morning our guide was so ill, and his limbs swelled so much with the rankling of his two wounds, that he could go no farther; so we were obliged to take a new guide here, and go to Toulouse, where we found a warm climate, a fruitful pleasant country, and no snow, no wolves, nor anything like them.

I was now come to the centre of my travels, and had in a little time all my new discovered estate safe about me; the bills of exchange which I brought with me having been very currently paid.

My principal guide and privy counsellor was my good ancient widow; who, in gratitude for the money I had sent her, thought no pains too much, nor care too great, to employ for me; and I trusted her so entirely with everything, that I was perfectly easy as to the security of my effects.

I now resolved to dispose of my plantation in the Brazils, if I could find means. For this purpose, I wrote to my old friend at Lisbon, who having offered it to the two merchants, the survivors of my trustees, who lived in the Brazils, they accepted the offer, and remitted thirty-three thousand pieces of eight to a correspondent of theirs at Lisbon, to pay for it.

Though I had sold my estate in the Brazils, yet I could not keep the country out of my head; nor could I resist the strong inclination I had to see my island. My true friend, the widow, earnestly dissuaded me from it, and so far prevailed with me, that, for almost seven years, she prevented my running abroad; during which time I took my two nephews, the children of one of my brothers, into my care: the eldest having something of his own, I bred up as a gentleman, and gave him a settlement of some addition to his estate, after my decease. The other I put out to a captain of a ship; and after five years, finding him a sensible, bold, enterprising young fellow, I put him into a good ship, and sent him to sea: and this young fellow afterwards drew me in, old as I was, to further adventures myself.

In the meantime, I in part settled myself here: for, first of all I married, and that not either to my disadvantage or dissatisfaction, and had three children, two sons and one daughter; but my wife dying, and my nephew coming home with good success from a voyage to Spain, my inclination to go abroad, and his importunity prevailed, and engaged me to go in his ship as a private trader to the East Indies; this was in the year 1694.

SECTION XXX

HE IS SEIZED WITH A DESIRE TO REVISIT HIS ISLAND—IS TEMPTED TO GO TO SEA AGAIN—TAKES OUT A CARGO FOR HIS COLONY

WHEN my wife was gone, the world looked awkwardly round me. I was as much a stranger in it, in my thoughts, as I was in the Brazils, when I first went on shore there; and as much alone, except as to assistance of servants, as I was in my island. I knew neither what to think nor what to do.

My sage counsellor was gone; I was like a ship without a pilot, that could only run before the wind: my thoughts ran all away again into the whole affair; my head was quite turned with the whimsies of foreign adventures.

It was now the beginning of the year 1693, when my nephew, whom, as I have observed before, I had brought up to the sea, and had made him commander of a ship, was come home, from a short voyage to Bilboa, being the first he had made. He came to me, and told me that some merchants of his acquaintance had been proposing to him to go a voyage to the East Indies and to China, as private traders. "And now, uncle," says he, "if you will go to sea with me, I will engage to land you upon your old habitation in the island, for we are to touch at the Brazils."

The scheme hit so exactly with my temper, that is to say, the prepossession I was under, and of which I have said so much, that I told him, in a few words, if he agreed with the merchants I would go with him; but I told him I would not promise to go any farther than my own island. "Why, sir," says he, "you don't want to be left there again, I hope?" "Why," said I, "can you not take me up again on your return?"

He told me it would not be possible to do so; that the merchants would never allow him to come that way with a laden ship of such value, it being a month's sail out of his way, and might be three or four. "Besides, sir, if I should miscarry," said he, "and not return at all, then you would be just reduced to the condition you were in before."

This was very rational; but we both found out a remedy for it; which was to carry a framed sloop on board the ship, which being taken in pieces, and shipped on board the ship, might, by the help of some carpenters, whom we agreed to carry with us, be set up again in the island and finished, fit to go to sea, in a few days.

I was not long resolving; for, indeed, the importunities of my nephew joined so effectually with my inclination, that nothing could oppose me; on the other hand, my wife being dead, I had nobody concerning themselves so much for me as to persuade me to one way or the other, except my ancient good friend the widow, who earnestly struggled with me to consider my years, my easy circumstances, and the needless hazards of a long voyage, and above all, my young children. But it was all to no purpose;

I had an irresistible desire to the voyage; and I told her I thought there was something so uncommon in the impressions I had upon my mind for the voyage, that it would be a kind of resisting Providence if I should attempt to stay at home; after which she ceased her expostulations, and joined with me, not only in making provision for my voyage, but also in settling my family affairs for my absence, and providing for the education of my children.

In order to this, I made my will, and settled the estate I had in such a manner for my children, and placed in such hands, that I was perfectly easy and satisfied they would have justice done them, whatever might befall me; and for their education, I left it wholly to the widow, with a sufficient maintenance to herself for her care: all of which she richly deserved, for no mother could have taken more care in her education, or understood it better; and as she lived till I came home, I also lived to thank her for it.

My nephew was ready to sail about the beginning of January, 1694–5 and I, with my man Friday, went on board in the Downs on the 8th; having, besides that sloop which I mentioned above, a very considerable cargo of all kinds of necessary things for my colony, which, if I did not find in good condition, I resolved to leave so.

Contrary winds first put us to the northward, and we were obliged to put in at Galway in Ireland, where we lay wind-bound two and twenty days; but we had the satisfaction with the disaster, that provisions were here exceeding cheap, and in the utmost plenty; so that while we lay here, we never touched the ship's stores, but rather added to them. Here also I took in several live hogs, and two cows, with their calves, which I resolved, if I had a good passage to put on shore in my island; but we found occasion to dispose otherwise of them.

We set out on the 5th of February from Ireland. I shall trouble nobody with the little incidents of wind, weather, currents, etc., on our voyage; but to shorten my story, for the sake of what is to follow, shall observe, that I came to my old habitation, the island, on the 10th of April, 1695. It was with no small difficulty that I found the place; for as I came to it, and went from it, before on the south and east side of the island, as coming from the Brazils, so now, coming in between the main and the island, and having no chart for the coast, nor any landmark, I did not know it when I saw it, or know whether I saw it or not.

Thus coasting from one island to another, sometimes with the ship, sometimes with the Frenchmen's shallop, which we had found a convenient boat, and therefore kept her with their very good-will, at length I came fair on the south side of my island, and presently knew the very countenance of the place: so I brought the ship safe to an anchor, broadside with the little creek where my old habitation was.

SECTION XXXI

ROBINSON AND FRIDAY GO ASHORE—THE LATTER MEETS WITH HIS FATHER—ACCOUNT OF WHAT PASSED ON THE ISLAND AFTER ROBINSON'S QUITTING IT

As soon as I saw the place, I called for Friday, and asked him if he knew where he was; he looked about a little, and presently clapping his hands, cried: "O yes, O there, O yes, O there," pointing to our old habitation, and fell dancing and capering like a mad fellow; and I had much ado to keep him from jumping into the sea, to swim ashore to the place.

"Well, Friday," says I, "do you think we shall find anybody here or no? and do you think we shall see your father?" The fellow stood mute as a stock a good while, but when I named his father, the poor affectionate creature looked dejected, and I could see the tears ran down his face very plentifully. "What is the matter Friday?" says I, "are you troubled because you may see your father?" "No, no," says he, shaking his head, "no see him more: no, never more see him again." "Why so," said I, "Friday, how do you know that?" "O no, O no," says Friday, "he long ago die, long ago, he much old man." "Well, well," says I, "Friday, you don't know; but shall we see anyone else, then?" The fellow, it seems, had better eyes than I, and he points to the hill just above my old house; and though we lay half a league off, he cries out, "We see, we see, yes, yes, we see much man there, and there, and there." I looked, but I saw nobody; no, not with a perspective glass, which was, I suppose, because I could not hit the place; for the fellow was right, as I found upon inquiry the next day; and there were five or six men all together, who stood to look at the ship, not knowing what to think of us.

As we went on shore upon the tide of flood, near high water, we rowed directly into the creek; and the first man that I fixed my eye upon was the Spaniard whose life I had saved, and whom I knew by his face perfectly well: as to his habit, I shall describe it afterwards. I ordered nobody to go on shore but myself; but there was no keeping Friday in the boat, for the affectionate creature had spied his father at a distance, a good way off the Spaniards, where indeed I saw nothing of him; and if they had not let him go ashore, he would have jumped into the sea. He was no sooner on shore, but he flew away to his father, like an arrow out of a bow. It would have made any man shed tears, in spite of the firmest resolution, to have seen the first transports of this poor fellow's joy when he came to his father.

It would be needless to take notice of all the ceremonies and civilities that the Spaniards received me with. The first Spaniard, who, as I said, I knew very well, was he whose life I had saved; he came towards the boat, and he not only did not know me at first, but he had no thoughts, no notion of its being me that was come, till I spoke to him. "Senhor," said I, in Portuguese, "do you not know me?" At which he spoke not a word, but giving his musket to the man that was with him, threw his arms abroad, saying something in Spanish that I did not perfectly hear, came forward and embraced me; telling me he was inexcusable not to know the face again; then beckoning to the person that attended him, bade him go and call out his comrades. He then asked me if I would walk to my old habitation, where he would give me possession of my own house again, and where I should see they had made but mean improvements: so I walked along with him; but, alas! I could no more find the place again than if I had never been there; for they had planted so many trees, and placed them in such a posture, so thick and close to one another, and in ten years' time they were grown so big, that in short, the place was inaccessible, except by such windings and blind ways as they themselves only, who made them, could find.

I asked them what put them upon all these fortifications: he told me I would say there was need enough of it, when he had given me an account how they had passed their time since their arriving in the island, especially after they had the misfortune to find that I was gone.

As to the three barbarians (so he called them) that were left behind, and of whom he said he had a long story to tell me, the Spaniards all thought themselves much better among the savages, only that their number was so small: and, says he, had they been strong enough, we had been all long ago in purgatory; and with that he crossed himself on the breast. "But sir," says he, "I hope you will not be displeased when I shall tell you how, forced by necessity, we were obliged, for our own preservation, to disarm them, and make them our subjects, who would not be content with being moderately our masters, but would be our murderers." I answered: "I was heartily afraid of it when I left them there, and nothing troubled me at my parting from the island but that they were not come back, that I might have put them in possession of everything first, and left the others in a state of subjection, as they deserved; but if they had reduced them to it, I was very glad, and should be very far from finding any fault with it; for I knew they were a parcel of refractory, ungoverned villains, and were fit for any manner of mischief."

While I was saying this, the man came whom he had sent back, and with him eleven men more. In the dress they were in, it was impossible to guess what nation they were of; but he made all clear, both to them and to me. First he turned to me, and pointing to them, said, "These, sir, are some of the gentlemen who owe their lives to you"; and then turning to them, and pointing to me, he let them know who I was; upon which they all came up, one by one, not as if they had been sailors and ordinary fellows, and the like, but really as if they had been ambassadors of noblemen, and I a monarch or great conqueror.

I shall no longer trouble the story with a relation in the

first person, which will put me to the expense of ten thousand *said I's* and *said ye's*, and *he told me's*, and *I told him's*, and the like; but I shall collect the facts historically, as near as I can gather them out of my memory, from what they related to me, and from what I met with in my conversing with them and with the place.

The first thing, however, which I inquired into, that I might begin where I left off, was of their own part; and I desired he would give me a particular account of his voyage back to his countrymen with the boat, when I sent him to fetch them over. He told me there was but little variety in that part, for nothing remarkable happened to them on the way, having had very calm weather and a smooth sea. As for his countrymen, it could not be doubted, he said, but that they were overjoyed to see him (it seems he was the principal man among them, the captain of the vessel they had been shipwrecked in having been dead some time); they were, he said, the more surprised to see him, because they knew that he was fallen into the hands of savages, who, they were satisfied, would devour him, as they did all the rest of their prisoners; that when he told them the story of his deliverance, and in what manner he was furnished for carrying them away, it was like a dream to them.

Their first business was to get canoes: and in this they were obliged not to stick so much upon the honest part of it, but to trespass upon their friendly savages, and to borrow two large canoes, or periaguas, on pretence of going a-fishing, or for pleasure. In these they came away the next morning. It seems they wanted no time to get themselves ready; for they had no baggage, neither clothes nor provisions, nor anything in the world but what they had on them, and a few roots to eat, of which they used to make their bread.

They were in all three weeks absent, and in that time unluckily for them, I had the occasion offered for my escape, as I mentioned in my other part, and to get off from the island, leaving three of the most impudent, hardened, ungoverned, disagreeable villains behind me, that any man could desire to meet with; to the poor Spaniards' great grief and disappointment, you may be sure.

The only just thing the rogues did was, that when the

Spaniards came ashore, they gave my letter to them, and gave them provisions, and other relief, as I had ordered them to do; also they gave them the long paper of directions which I had left with them, containing the methods for managing my life there; nor did they refuse to accommodate the Spaniards with anything else, for they agreed very well for some time. They gave them an equal admission into the house, or cave, and they began to live very sociably; and the head Spaniard, who had seen pretty much of my methods, and Friday's father together managed all their affairs: but as for the Englishmen, they did nothing but ramble about the island, shoot parrots and catch tortoises; and when they came home at night, the Spaniards provided their suppers for them.

The Spaniards would have been satisfied with this, had the others but let them alone; which, however, they could not find in their hearts to do long, but, like the dog in the manger, they would not eat themselves, neither would they let the others eat. The differences, nevertheless, were at first but trivial, and such as are not worth relating, but at last it broke out into open war.

But before I come to the particulars of this part, I must supply a defect in my former relation; and this was, I forgot to set down, among the rest, that just as we were weighing the anchor to set sail, there happened a little quarrel on board of our ship, which I was afraid would have turned to a second mutiny; nor was it appeased till the captain, rousing up his courage, and taking us all to his assistance, parted them by force, and making two of the most refractory fellows prisoners, he laid them in irons; and as they had been active in the former disorders and let fall some ugly, dangerous words, the second time he threatened to carry them in irons to England, and have them hanged there for mutiny and running away with the ship. This it seems, though the captain did not intend to do it, frightened some other men in the ship; and some of them had put it into the heads of the rest that the captain only gave them good words for the present, till they should come to some English port, and that then they should be all put into gaol and tried for their lives. The mate got intelligence of this, and acquainted us with it; upon which it was desired that I, who still passed for a great man among them, should go down with the mate and satisfy the men, and tell them that they might be assured, if they behaved well the rest of the voyage, all they had done for the time past should be pardoned. So I went, and after passing my honour's word to them, they appeared easy, and the more so when I caused the two men that were in irons to be released and forgiven.

But this mutiny had brought us to an anchor for that night; the wind also falling calm next morning, we found that our two men who had been laid in irons had stole each of them a musket, and some other weapons (what powder and shot they had we knew not), and had taken the ship's pinnace, which was not yet hauled up, and run away with her to their companions in roguery on shore. These two men made their number five; but the other three villains were so much more wicked than they, that after they had been two or three days together, they turned the two new-comers out of doors to shift for themselves, and would have nothing to do with them; nor could they, for a good while, be persuaded to give them any food: as for the Spaniards, they were not yet come.

When the Spaniards came first on shore, the business began to go forward: the Spaniards would have persuaded the three English brutes to have taken in their two countrymen again, that, as they said, they might be all one family; but they would not hear of it: so the two poor fellows lived by themselves; and finding nothing but industry and application would make them live comfortably, they pitched their tents on the north shore of the island, but a little more to the west, to be out of danger of the savages, who always landed on the east parts of the island.

Here they built them two huts, one to lodge in and the other to lay up their magazines and stores in; and the Spaniards having given them some corn for seed, and especially some of the peas which I had left them, they dug, planted and enclosed after the pattern I had set for them all, and began to live pretty well.

SECTION XXXII

THE ACCOUNT CONTINUED—QUARRELS BETWEEN THE ENGLISHMEN—A BATTLE BETWEEN TWO PARTIES OF SAVAGES WHO VISIT THE ISLAND—FRESH MUTINY AMONG THE SETTLERS

THEY were going on in this little thriving posture, when the three unnatural rogues, their own countrymen too, in mere humour and to insult them, came and bullied them, and told them the island was theirs; that the Governor, meaning me, had given them the possession of it, and nobody else had any right to it; and that they should build no houses upon their ground unless they would pay rent for them.

The two men, thinking they were jesting at first, asked them to come in and sit down, and see what fine houses they had built, and to tell them what rent they demanded. One of the three, cursing and raging, told them they should see they were not in jest; and going to a little place at a distance, where the honest men had made a fire to dress their victuals, he takes a fire-brand, and claps it to the outside of their hut, and very fairly set it on fire; and it would have been burned all down in a few minutes, if one of the two had not run to the fellow, thrust him away, and trod the fire out with his feet.

The fellow was in such a rage at the honest man's thrusting him away, that he returned upon him, with a pole he had in his hand, and had not the man avoided the blow very nimbly, and run into the hut, he had ended his days at once. His comrade, seeing the danger they were both in, ran in after him, and immediately they both came out with their muskets, and the man that was first struck at with the pole knocked the fellow down that had begun the quarrel, with the stock of his musket, and that before the other two could come to help him; and then seeing the rest come at them, they stood together, and presenting the other ends of their pieces to them, bade them stand off.

The others had fire-arms with them too, but one of the two honest men, bolder than his comrade, and made desperate by his danger, told them, if they offered to move hand or foot they were dead men, and boldly commanded them to lay down their arms. They did not, indeed, lay down their arms, but seeing him so resolute it brought them to a parley, and they consented to take their wounded man with them and be gone; and, indeed, it seems the fellow was wounded sufficiently with the blow. However, they were much in the wrong, since they had the advantage, that they did not disarm them effectually, as they might have done, and have gone immediately to the Spaniards, and given them an account of how the rogues had treated them; for the three villains studied nothing but revenge, and every day gave some intimation that they did so.

But not to crowd this part with an account of the lesser part of the rogueries, such as treading down their corn; shooting three young kids and a she-goat, which the poor men had got to breed up tame for their store; and, in a word, plaguing them night and day in this manner; it forced the two men to such a desperation, that they resolved to fight them all three, the first time they had a fair opportunity. In order to this, they resolved to go to the castle, as they called it (that was my old dwelling), where the three rogues and the Spaniards all lived together at that time, intending to have a fair battle, and the Spaniards should stand by, to see fair play; so they got up in the morning before day, and came to the place, and called the Englishmen by their names, telling a Spaniard that answered that they wanted to speak with them.

It happened that the day before, two of the Spaniards, having been in the woods, had seen one of the two Englishmen, whom, for distinction, I called the honest men, and he had made a sad complaint to the Spaniards of the barbarous usage they had met with from their three countrymen, and how they had ruined their plantation, and destroyed their corn that they had laboured so hard to bring forward, and killed the milch goat and their three kids, which was all they had provided for their sustenance; and that if he and his friends, meaning the Spaniards, did not assist them again, they should be starved. When the Spaniards came home at night, and they were all at supper, one of them took the freedom to reprove the three Englishmen, though in very gentle and mannerly terms, and asked them how they could be so cruel, they being harmless, inoffensive fellows.

One of the Englishmen returned very briskly: "What had they to do there? that they came on shore without leave; and that they should not plant or build upon the island; it was none of their ground." "Why," says the Spaniard, very calmly, "Senhor Inglese, they must not starve." The Englishman replied, like a rough-hewn tarpauling: "They might starve and be hanged; they should not plant nor build in that place." "But what must they do then, senhor?" said the Spaniard. Another of the brutes returned: "Do? they should be servants, and work for them." "But how can you expect that of them?" says the Spaniard; "they are not bought with your money: you have no right to make them servants." The Englishman answered: "The island was theirs; the Governor had given it to them, and no man had anything to do there but themselves"; and with that swore by his Maker that they would go and burn all their new huts; they should build none upon their land. "Why, senhor," says the Spaniard, "by the same rule we must be your servants too." "Ay," says the bold dog, "and so you shall too before we have done with you." The Spaniard only smiled at that, and made him no answer. However, this little discourse had heated them; and starting up one says to the other, I think it was he they called Will Atkins: "Come, Jack, let's go, and have 'tother brush with 'em; we'll demolish their castle, I'll warrant you; they shall plant no colony in our dominions."

Upon this they went all trooping away, with every man a gun, a pistol and a sword, and muttered some insolent things among themselves, of what they would do to the Spaniards too, when opportunity offered; but the Spaniards it seems, did not so perfectly understand them as to know all the particulars, only that in general they threatened them hard for taking the two Englishmen's part.

Whither they went, or how they bestowed their time that evening, the Spaniards said they did not know; but it seems they wandered about the country part of the night, and then lying down in the place which I used to call my bower, they were weary and overslept themselves. The case was this: they had resolved to stay till midnight, and so take the two poor men when they were asleep, and, as they acknowledged afterwards, intended to set fire to their huts while they were in them, and either burn them there, or murder them as they came out.

However, as the two men had also a design upon them, as I have said, though a much fairer one than that of burning and murdering, it happened, and very luckily for them all, that they were up, and gone abroad, before the bloody-minded rogues came to their huts.

When they came there, and found the men gone, Atkins, who, it seems, was the forwardest man, called out to his comrade: "Ha, Jack, here's the nest, but the birds are flown." They mused awhile to think what should be the occasion of their being gone abroad so soon, and suggested presently that the Spaniards had given them notice of it; and with that they shook hands, and swore to one another that they would be revenged of the Spaniards. As soon as they had made this bloody bargain, they fell to work with the poor men's habitation; they did not set fire, indeed, to anything, but they pulled down both their houses, and tore all their little collected household stuff in pieces, and in a word sacked and plundered everything as completely as a horde of Tartars would have done.

The two men were, at this juncture, gone to find them out, and had resolved to fight them wherever they had been, though they were but two to three; so that, had they met, there certainly would have been bloodshed among them; for they were all very stout, resolute fellows, to give them their due.

But Providence took more care to keep them asunder than they themselves could do to meet. When the three came back like furious creatures, they came up to the Spaniards, and one of them, stepping up to one of the Spaniards, as if they had been a couple of boys at play takes hold of his hat as it was upon his head, and giving it a twirl about, fleering in his face, says to him: "And you, Senhor Jack Spaniard shall have the same sauce if you do not mend your manners." The Spaniard, who, though a quiet, civil man, was as brave a man as could be, and withal a strong, well-made man, looked at him for a good while, and then having no weapon in his hand, stepped gravely up to him, and with one blow of his fist knocked him down, as an ox is felled with a pole-axe; at which one of the rogues, as insolent as the first, fired his pistol at the Spaniard immediately: he missed his body, indeed, for the bullets went through his hair, but one of them touched the tip of his ear, and he bled pretty much. The blood made the Spaniard believe he was more hurt than he really was, and that put him into some heat, for before he acted all in a perfect calm; but now, resolving to go through with his work, he stooped, and took the fellow's musket whom he had knocked down, and was just going to shoot the man who had fired at him, when the rest of the Spaniards, being in the cave, came out, and calling to him not to shoot, they stepped in, secured the other two and took their arms from them.

When they were thus disarmed, and found they had made all the Spaniards their enemies, as well as their own countrymen, they began to cool, and giving the Spaniard better words, would have their arms again; but the Spaniards, considering the feud that was between them and the other two Englishmen, and that it would be the best method they could take to keep them from killing one another, told them they would do them no harm, and if they would live peaceably, they would be very willing to assist and associate with them as they did before; but that they could not think of giving them their arms again.

The rogues were now no more capable to hear reason than to act with reason; but being refused their arms, they went raving away, and raging like madmen, threatening what they would do, though they had no fire-arms. As soon as they were gone, the two men came back in passion and rage enough also, though of another kind; for, having been at their plantation, and finding it all demolished and destroyed as above, it will easily be supposed they had provocation enough. They could scarce have room to tell their tale, the Spaniards were so eager to tell theirs. And it was strange enough to find that three men should thus bully nineteen, and receive no punishment at all.

The Spaniards, indeed, despised them, and especially, having thus disarmed them, made light of their threatenings; but the two Englishmen resolved to have their remedy against them, what pains soever it cost to find them out. But the Spaniards interposed here too, and told them, that as they had disarmed them, they could not consent that they (the two) should pursue them with fire-arms, and perhaps kill them. " But," said the grave Spaniard, who was their governor, " we will endeavour to make them do you justice, if you leave it to us." The two Englishmen yielded to this very awkwardly, and with great reluctance; but the Spaniards protested they did it only to keep them from bloodshed, and to make all easy at last.

In about five days' time the three vagrants, tired with wandering, and almost starved with hunger, having chiefly lived on turtles' eggs all that while, came back to the grove; and finding my Spaniard, who, as I have said, was the governor, and two more with him walking by the side of the creek, they came up in a very submissive, humble manner, and begged to be received again into the family. The Spaniards used them civilly, but told them they had acted so unnaturally by their countrymen, and so very grossly by them (the Spaniards), that they could not come to any conclusion without consulting the two Englishmen and the rest; but, however, they would go to them, and discourse about it.

After half an hour's consultation, they were called in, and a long debate ensued; their two countrymen charging them with the ruin of all their labour, and a design to murder them; all of which they owned before, and therefore could not deny now. Upon the whole, the Spaniards acted the moderator between them; and as they had obliged the two Englishmen not to hurt the three while they were naked and unarmed, so they now obliged the three to go and rebuild their fellows' two huts, one to be of the same, and the other of larger dimensions, than they were before; and, in a word, to restore everything in the state as they found it, as near as they could.

Well, they submitted to all this; and as they had plenty of provisions given them all the while, they grew very orderly, and thus having lived pretty well together for a month or two, the Spaniards gave them arms again. It was not above a week after they had these arms, and went abroad, but the ungrateful creatures began to be as insolent and troublesome as before: but, however, an accident happened presently upon this, which endangered the safety of them all, and they were obliged to lay by all private resentments, and look to the preservation of their lives.

It happened one night that the Spanish governor, as I call him, who was now the captain, or leader, or governor of the rest, found himself very uneasy in the night, and could by no means get any sleep: he lay a great while, but growing more and more uneasy, he resolved to rise. Being thus got up, he looked out; but, being dark, he could see little or nothing; and laid him down again; but it was all one, he could not sleep, nor could he compose himself to anything like rest.

Having made some noise with rising and walking about, going out and coming in, another of them waked and calling, asked who it was that was up. The governor told him how it had been with him. "Say you so?" says the other Spaniard; "such things are not to be slighted, I assure you; there is certainly some mischief working near us. Come," says he, "let us go and look abroad; and if we find nothing at all in it to justify the trouble, I'll tell you a story to the purpose, that shall convince you of the justice of my proposing it."

In a word, they went out to go to the top of the hill where I used to go; but they being strong and a good company, not alone, as I was, used none of my cautions, to go up by the ladder, and pulling it up after them, to go up a second stage to the top, but were going round through the grove, unconcerned and unwary, when they were surprised with seeing a light as of fire, a very little way from them, and hearing the voices of men, not one or two, but of a great number.

How so great a number came now together, or whether they came ignorantly and by accident, on their usual bloody errand, the Spaniards could not, it seems, understand; but whatever it was, it had been their business either to have concealed themselves, or not to have seen them at all, much less to have let the savages have seen that there were any inhabitants in the place; or to have fallen upon them so effectually, as that not a man of them should have escaped, which could only have been by getting in between them and their boats; but this presence of mind was wanting to them, which was the ruin of their tranquillity for a great while.

We need not doubt but that the governor and the man with him, surprised with this sight, ran back immediately, and raised their fellows, giving them an account of the imminent danger they were all in, and they again as readily took the alarm; but it was impossible to persuade them to stay close within, where they were, but they must all run out to see how things stood.

The Spaniards were in no small consternation at this sight; and they were in great perplexity also for fear of their flock of goats, which would have been little less than starving them, if they should have been destroyed; so the first thing they resolved upon was to despatch three men away before it was light, two Spaniards and one Englishman, to drive all the goats away to the great valley where the cave was.

They then resolved, while it was still dark, to send the old savage, Friday's father, out as a spy, to learn, if possible something concerning them. After he had been gone an hour or two, he brought word that he had been among them undiscovered; that he found they were two parties, and of two separate nations, who had war with one another, and had a great battle in their own country; and that both sides having had several prisoners taken in the fight, they were, by mere chance, landed all on the same island, for the devouring of their prisoners and making merry, but their coming so by chance to the same place had spoiled all their mirth; that they were in a great rage at one another, and were so near, that he believed they would fight again as soon as daylight began to appear.

The battle held two hours before they could guess which party would be beaten; but then that which was nearest our people's habitation began to appear weakest, and after some time more, some of them began to fly; and this put our men again into a great consternation, lest any one of those that fled should run into the grove before their dwelling for shelter, and thereby involuntarily discover the place; and that, by consequence, the pursuers would do the like in search of them.

As they expected, it fell out: three of the routed army fled for life, and crossing the creek, ran directly into the place, not in the least knowing whither they went, but running as into a thick wood for shelter. The conquerors did not pursue them, or see which way they were gone: upon this the Spaniard Governor, a man of humanity, would not suffer them to kill these fugitives. The residue of the conquered people fled to their canoes; the victors retired, made no pursuit, or very little, but drawing themselves into a body together, gave two screaming shouts, which they supposed was by the way of triumph, and so the fight ended: and the same day, about three o'clock in the afternoon, they also marched to their canoes.

After they were all gone, the Spaniards came out of their den, and viewing the field of battle, they found about two-and-thirty men dead on the spot. They found not one man that was not stone-dead, for either they stay by their enemy till they have quite killed him, or they carry all the wounded men that are not quite dead away with them.

This deliverance, as I said, tamed even the three English brutes I have been speaking of, and for a great while after they were tractable, and went about the common business of the whole society well enough; planted, sowed, reaped, and began to be all naturalised to the country. But some time after this, they fell into such measures again, as brought them into a great deal of trouble.

But to come to the family part. Being all now good friends, for common danger, as I said above, had effectually reconciled them, they began to consider their general circumstances; and the first thing that came under their consideration was whether, seeing the savages particularly haunted that side of the island, there were not more remote and retired parts of it equally adapted to their way of living.

Upon this, after long debate, it was concluded that they would not remove their habitation; because that, some time or other, they thought they might hear from their governor again, meaning me, but as to their corn and cattle they agreed to remove them into the valley where my cave was; and as I had carefully covered my habitation first with a wall or fortification, and then with a grove of trees, so seeing their safety consisted entirely in their being concealed, of which they were now fully convinced, they set to work to cover and conceal the place yet more effectually than before.

I return to my story. They lived two years after this in perfect retirement, and had no more visits from the savages. And now they had another broil with the three Englishmen; one of them, a most turbulent fellow, being in a rage at one of the three savages, which I mentioned they had taken, because the fellow did not do something right which he bid him do, and seemed a little untractable in his showing him, drew a hatchet out of his frog-belt, in which he wore it by his side, and fell upon the poor savage, not to correct him, but to kill him. One of the Spaniards who was by, seeing him give the fellow a barbarous cut with the hatchet, which he aimed at his head, but struck into his shoulder so that he thought he had cut the poor creature's arm off, ran to him and entreating him not to murder the poor man, placed himself between him and the savage, to prevent the mischief. The fellow being enraged the more at this, struck at the Spaniard, who avoided the blow, and with a shovel which he had in his hand, knocked the brute down. Another of the Englishmen running at the same time to help his comrade, knocked the Spaniard down; and then two more Spaniards came on to help their man, and a third Englishman fell in upon them This fray set the whole family in an uproar, and more help coming in, they took the three Englishmen prisoners. The next question was, what should be done with them?

The Spaniard who was governor told them in so many words that if they had been of his own country, he would have hanged them; for all laws and all governors were to preserve society, and those who were dangerous to the society ought to be expelled out of it; but as they were Englishmen, and it was to the generous kindness of an Englishman that they all owed their preservation and deliverance, he would leave them to the judgment of the other two Englishmen who were their countrymen.

One of the two honest Englishmen stood up, and said they desired it might not be left to them: "For," says he, "I am sure we ought to sentence them to the gallows"; and with that he gives an account of how Will Atkins, one of the three, had proposed to have all the five Englishmen join together, and murder all the Spaniards when they were in their sleep.

When the Spanish governor heard this, he calls to Will

Atkins: "How, Senhor Atkins, would you murder us all? What have you to say to that?" The hardened villain was so far from denying it, that he said it was true: and that they would do it still before they had done with them. "Well, but, Senhor Atkins," says the Spaniard, "must we kill you, or you kill us? Why will you put us to the necessity of this?" Atkins was in such a rage at the Spaniard's making a jest of it that, had he not been held by three men, and withal had no weapon near him, it was thought he would have attempted to have killed the Spaniard in the middle of all the company.

After a long debate, it was agreed, first that they should be disarmed, and not permitted to have either gun, powder, shot, sword, or any weapon; and should be turned out of the society and left to live where they would, and how they would, by themselves; and if they offered to commit any disorder, so as to spoil, burn, kill, or destroy any of the corn, plantings, buildings, fences, or cattle belonging to the society, they should die without mercy, and they would shoot them wherever they could find them.

About three quarters of a year after this separation, a new frolic took these rogues, which, together with the former villainy they had committed, brought mischief enough upon them, and had very nearly been the ruin of the whole colony.

SECTION XXXIII

THE MUTINOUS ENGLISHMEN DISMISSED FROM THE ISLAND—RETURN WITH SEVERAL CAPTIVE SAVAGES—TAKE THE FEMALES AS WIVES—ARRIVAL OF SAVAGES

THE three fellows came down to the Spaniards one morning, and in very humble terms desired to be admitted to speak with them; the Spaniards very readily heard what they had to say, which was this: That they were tired of living in the manner they did; and that they were not handy enough to make the necessaries they wanted, and that having no help, they found they should be starved; but if the Spaniards would give them leave to take one of the canoes which they came over in, they would go over to the main and seek their fortunes.

The Spaniards told them, with great kindness, that if they were resolved to go, they should not go like naked men, and be in no condition to defend themselves: and that though they could ill spare their fire-arms, having not enough for themselves, yet they would let them have two muskets, a pistol, and a cutlass, and each man a hatchet, which they thought was sufficient for them.

After two-and-twenty days' absence one of the Englishmen, being abroad upon his planting work, sees three strange men coming towards him, with guns upon their shoulders. Away runs the Englishman, as if he was bewitched, comes frightened and amazed to the governor Spaniard, and tells him that they were all undone, for there were strangers landed upon the island, but could not tell who.

While they were debating this, came the three Englishmen, and standing without the wood, which was new planted, hallooed to them; they presently knew their voices, and so all the wonder of that kind ceased. But now the admiration was turned upon another question, viz., What could be the matter, and what made them come back again?

It was not long before they brought the men in, and inquiring where they had been and what they had been doing, they gave them a full account of their voyage in a few words, viz., that they reached the land in two days, or something less; but finding the people alarmed at their coming, and preparing with bows and arrows to fight them, they durst not go on shore, but sailing on to the northward they saw another island, and several more west; and having resolved to land somewhere, they put over to one of the islands which lay west, and went boldly on shore: there they found the people very courteous and friendly to them.

They continued here four days; and inquired, as well as they could of them, by signs, what nations were this way, and that way; and were told of several fierce and terrible people that lived almost every way, who, as they made known by signs to them, used to eat men; but as for themselves, they said, they never ate men or women, except only such as they took in the wars, and then, they owned, they made a great feast and ate their prisoners.

The Englishmen inquired when they had a feast of that kind; and they told them about two moons ago, pointing to the moon, and to two fingers; and that their great king had two hundred prisoners now, which he had taken in his war, and they were feeding them to make them fat for the next feast. The Englishmen seemed mighty desirous of seeing those prisoners; but the others mistaking them, thought they were desirous to have some of them to carry away for their own eating; and accordingly, the next morning, they brought down five women and eleven men, and gave them to the Englishmen to carry with them on their voyage, just as we would bring so many cows and oxen down to a seaport town to victual a ship.

Having taken their leave, with all the respect and thanks that could well pass between people, where on either side, they understood not one word they could say, they put off with their boat, and came back towards the first island; where, when they arrived, they set eight of their prisoners at liberty. They first of all unbound them; but the poor creatures screamed at that, especially the women, for they concluded they were unbound on purpose to be killed. If they gave them anything to eat it was the same thing; they then concluded it was for fear they should sink in flesh, and so not be fat enough to kill. If they looked at one of them more particularly, the party presently concluded it was to see whether he or she was fattest, and fittest to kill first; nay, after they had brought them quite over, and begun to use them kindly, and treat them well, still they expected every day to make a dinner or supper for their new masters.

When the three wanderers had given this unaccountable history or journal of their voyage, the Spaniard asked them where their new family was; and being told that they had brought them on shore, and put them into one of their huts, and were come up to beg some victuals for them, they (the Spaniards) and the other two Englishmen, that is to say, the whole colony, resolved to go all down to the place and see them; and did so, and Friday's father with them.

When they came into the hut, there they sat all bound,

for when they had brought them on shore, they bound their hands, that they might not take the boat and make their escape; there, I say, they sat, all of them, stark naked. First, there were three men, lusty, comely fellows, well-shaped, straight and fair limbs, about thirty to thirty-five years of age; and five women, whereof two might be from thirty to forty; two more, not above four or five-and-twenty; and the fifth, a tall, comely maiden, about sixteen or seventeen. The women were well-favoured, agreeable persons, both in shape and features, only tawny; and two of them, had they been perfect white, would have passed for very handsome women, even in London itself, having pleasant, agreeable countenances, and of a very modest behaviour, especially when they came afterwards to be clothed and dressed, as they called it; though that dress was very indifferent, it must be confessed.

The first thing they did was to cause the old Indian, Friday's father, to go in, and see first if he knew any of them, and then, if he understood any of their speech. As soon as the old man came in, he looked seriously at them, but knew none of them; neither could any of them understand a word he said, or a sign he could make, except one of the women. However, this was enough to answer the end, which was to satisfy them that the men into whose hands they were fallen were Christians; that they abhorred eating men or women; and that they might be sure they would not be killed. As soon as they were assured of this, they discovered such a joy, and by such awkward gestures, several ways, as is hard to describe; for it seems they were of several nations.

The woman who was their interpreter was bid, in the next place, to ask them if they were willing to be servants, and to work for the men who had brought them away, to save their lives; at which they all fell a dancing; and presently one fell to taking up this, and another that, anything that lay next, to carry on their shoulders, to intimate that they were willing to work.

The governor, who found that the having women among them would presently be attended with some inconvenience, and might occasion some strife, and perhaps blood, asked the three men what they intended to do with these women, and whether they intended to make them servants or wives?

One of the Englishmen answered very boldly and readily, that they would make them both; to which the governor said: "I am not going to restrain you from it; you are your own masters as to that; but this I think is but just, for avoiding disorders and quarrels among you, and I desire it of you for that reason only, viz., that you will all engage that if any of you take any of these women, that while you stay here, the woman any of you takes, should be maintained by the man that takes her, and should be his wife." All this appeared so just, that every one agreed to it without any difficulty.

Then the Englishmen asked the Spaniards if they designed to take any of them? But every one of them answered no: some of them said they had wives in Spain, and the others did not like women that were not Christians; and all together declared that they would not have one of them. On the other hand, to be short, the five Englishmen took every one of them a wife; and so they set up a new form of living; for the Spaniards and Friday's father lived in my old habitation, which they had enlarged exceedingly within.

But the wonder of the story was, how five such refractory, ill-matched fellows should agree about these women, and that two of them should not pitch upon the same woman, especially seeing two or three of them were, without comparison, more agreeable than the others; but they took a good way enough to prevent quarrelling among themselves, for they set the five women by themselves in one of their huts, and they went all into the other hut, and drew lots among them who should choose first.

He that drew to choose first went away by himself to the hut where the poor naked creatures were, and fetched out her he chose; and it was worth observing, that he that chose first took her that was reckoned the homeliest and oldest of the five, which made mirth enough among the rest; and even the Spaniards laughed at it: but the fellow considered better than any of them, that it was application and business they were to expect assistance in, as much as in anything else; and she proved the best wife of all the parcel.

And here it is very well worth observing, that, as it often happens in the world (what the wise ends of God's providence are, in such a disposition of things, I cannot say), the two honest fellows had the two worst wives; and the three reprobates, that were scarce worth hanging, that were fit for nothing, and neither seemed born to do themselves good, nor any one else, had three clever, diligent, careful, and ingenious wives: not that the first two were bad wives, for all the five were most willing, quiet, passive, and subjected creatures, rather like slaves than wives; but my meaning is, they were not alike capable, ingenious, or industrious, or alike cleanly and neat.

But I now come to a scene different from all that had happened before, either to them or to me; and the original of the story was this: Early one morning there came on shore five or six canoes of Indians or savages, call them which you please, and there is no doubt they came upon the old errand of feeding upon their slaves; but that part was now so familiar to the Spaniards, and to our men too, that they did not concern themselves about it, as I did. They had nothing to do but to give notice to all the three plantations to keep within doors, and not show themselves, only placing a scout in a proper place, to give notice when the boats went to sea again.

This was, without doubt, very right; but a disaster spoiled all these measures, and made it known among the savages that there were inhabitants there; which was, in the end, the desolation of almost the whole colony. After the canoes with the savages were gone off, the Spaniards peeped abroad again; and some of them had the curiosity to go to the place where they had been to see what they had been doing. Here, to their great surprise, they found three savages left behind, and lying fast asleep upon the ground.

The Spaniards were greatly surprised at this sight and perfectly at a loss what to do. After some consultation, they resolved upon this: that they would lie still a while longer, till, if possible, these three men might be gone. But then the governor Spaniard recollected, that the three savages had no boat; and if they were left to rove about the island, they would certainly discover that there were inhabitants in it; and so they should be undone that way. Upon this they went back again, and there lay the fellows fast asleep still, and so they resolved to waken them, and take them prisoners; and they did so.

They carried them first to the bower, where was the chief of their country work, such as the keeping the goats, the planting the corn, etc., and afterwards they carried them to the habitation of the two Englishmen.

Here they were set to work, though it was not much they had for them to do; and whether it was by negligence in guarding them, or that they thought the fellows could not mend themselves, I know not, but one of them ran away, and taking to the woods, they could never hear of him any more.

They had good reason to believe he got home again soon after, in some other boats or canoes of savages who came on shore three or four weeks afterwards; and who, carrying on their revels as usual, went off in two days' time. This thought terrified them exceedingly; for they concluded, and that not without good cause indeed, that if this fellow came home safe among his comrades, he would certainly give them an account that there were people in the island, and also how few and weak they were.

The first testimony they had that this fellow had given intelligence of them was, that, about two months after this, six canoes of savages, with about seven, eight, or ten men in a canoe, came rowing along the north side of the island, where they never used to come before, and landed, about an hour after sunrise, at a convenient place, about a mile from the habitation of the two Englishmen, where this escaped man had been kept.

When the two poor frightened men had secured their wives and goods, they sent the other slave they had of the three who came with the women, and who was at the place by accident, away to the Spaniards with all speed, to give them the alarm, and desire speedy help; and, in the meantime, they took their arms and what ammunition they had, and retreated towards the place in the wood where their wives were sent; keeping at a distance, yet so that they might see, if possible, which way the savages took.

They had not gone far, but that from a rising ground they could see the little army of their enemies come on directly to their habitation, and, in a minute more, could see all their huts and household stuff flaming up together, to their great grief and mortification; for they had a very great loss, to them irretrievable, at least for some time

They kept their station for a while, till they found the savages, like wild beasts, spread themselves all over the place, rummaging every way and every place they could think of, in search of prey; and in particular for the people, of whom, now, it plainly appeared they had intelligence.

The two Englishmen seeing this, thinking themselves not secure where they stood, because it was likely some of the wild people might come that way, and they might come too many together, thought it proper to make another retreat about half a mile farther; believing, as it afterwards happened, that the farther they strolled the fewer would be together.

SECTION XXXIV

SEVERAL SAVAGES KILLED; THE REMAINDER LEAVE THE ISLAND—A FLEET OF THEM AFTERWARDS ARRIVE—A GENERAL BATTLE—THE SAVAGES ARE OVERCOME AND TRANQUILLITY RESTORED

THEIR next halt was at the entrance into a very thick-grown part of the woods and where an old trunk of a tree stood, which was hollow and vastly large; and in this tree they both took their standing, resolving to see there what might offer. They had not stood there long, before two of the savages appeared running directly that way, as if they already had noticed where they stood, and were coming up to attack them; and a little way farther they espied three more coming after them, and five more beyond them, all coming the same way; besides which, they saw seven or eight more at a distance running another way; for, in a word, they ran every way, like sportsmen beating for their game.

The poor men were now in great perplexity, but, after a very short debate with themselves, they resolved to stand them there; and if they were too many to deal with, then they would get up to the top of the tree, from whence they doubted not to defend themselves, fire excepted, as long as their ammunition lasted.

Having resolved upon this, they next considered whether

they should fire at the first two, or wait for the three, and so take the middle party, by which the two and the five that followed should be separated: at length they resolved to let the first two pass by, unless they should spy them in the tree, and come to attack them. The two first savages confirmed them also in this resolution, by turning a little from them towards another part of the wood; but the three, and the five after them, came forward directly to the tree, as if they had known the Englishmen were there.

While they were thus waiting, and the savages came on, they plainly saw that one of the three was the runaway savage that had escaped from them; and they both knew him distinctly, and resolved that, if possible, he should not escape, though they should both fire; so the other stood ready with his piece, that if he did not drop at the first shot, he should be sure to have a second. But the first was too good a marksman to miss his aim; for as the savages kept near one another, a little behind, in a line, he fired, and hit two of them directly: the foremost was killed outright, being shot in the head; the second, which was the runaway Indian, was shot through the body, and fell, but was not quite dead; and the third had a little scratch in the shoulder, perhaps by the same ball that went through the body of the second; and being dreadfully frightened, though not so much hurt, sat down upon the ground, screaming and yelling in a hideous manner.

The five that were behind, more frightened with the noise than sensible of the danger, stood still at first: for the woods made the sound a thousand times bigger than it really was, the echoes rattling from one side to another.

However, all being silent again, and they not knowing what the matter was, came on unconcerned, till they came to the place where their companions lay, in a condition miserable enough; and here the poor ignorant creatures, not sensible that they were within reach of the same mischief, stood all of a huddle over the wounded man, talking, and, as may be supposed, inquiring of him how he came to be hurt.

Our two men, though, as they confessed to me, it grieved them to be obliged to kill so many poor creatures, who, at the same time, had no notion of their danger; yet, having them all thus in their power, and the first having loaded his piece again, resolved to let fly both together among them; and singling out, by agreement, which to aim at, they shot together, and killed, or very much wounded, four of them: the fifth, frightened even to death, though not hurt, fell with the rest; so that our men, seeing them all fall together, thought they had killed them all.

The belief that the savages were all killed made our two men come boldly out from the tree before they had charged their guns, which was a wrong step; and they were under some surprise when they came to the place, and found no less than four of them alive, and of them two very little hurt, and one not at all: this obliged them to fall upon them with the stocks of their muskets; and first they made sure of the runaway savage, that had been the cause of all the mischief, and of another that was hurt in the knee, and put them out of their pain: then the man that was hurt not at all came and kneeled down to them, with his two hands held up, and made piteous moans to them, by gestures and signs, for his life, but could not say one word to them that they could understand. However, they made signs to him to sit down at the foot of a tree hard by; and one of the Englishmen, with a piece of rope twined, which he had by great chance in his pocket, tied his two hands behind him, and there they left him: and with what speed they could made after the other two, which were gone before, fearing they, or any more of them, should find the way to their covered place in the woods, where their wives, and the few goods they had left, lay. They came once in sight of the two men, but it was at a great distance; however, they had the satisfaction to see them cross over a valley towards the sea, quite the contrary way from that which led to their retreat, which they were afraid of; and being satisfied with that, they went back to the tree where they left their prisoner, who, as they supposed, was delivered by his comrades, for he was gone, and the two pieces of rope-yarn, with which they had bound him, lay just at the foot of the tree.

They were now in as great concern as before, not knowing what course to take, or how near the enemy might be, or in what numbers; so they resolved to go away to the place where their wives were, to see if all was well there.

When they came there, they found the savages had been

in the wood, and very near that place, but had not found it: for it was indeed inaccessible, by the trees standing so thick, as unless the persons seeking it had been directed by those that knew it, which these did not; they found, therefore, everything very safe, only the women in a terrible fright. While they were here, they had the comfort to have seven of the Spaniards come to their assistance; the other ten, with their servants, and old Friday, I mean Friday's father, were gone in a body to defend their bower, and the corn and cattle that was kept there. With the seven Spaniards came one of the three savages who, as I said, were their prisoners formerly; and with them also came the savage whom the Englishmen had left bound hand and foot at the tree: for it seems, they came that way, saw the slaughter of the seven men, and unbound the eighth, and brought him along with them.

When the Spaniards came, the two Englishmen were so encouraged, that they could not satisfy themselves to stay any longer there; but taking five of the Spaniards and themselves, with four muskets and a pistol among them and two stout quarter-staves, away they went in quest of the savages. And first they came to the tree where the men lay that had been killed; but it was easy to see that some more of the savages had been there, for they had attempted to carry their dead men away and had dragged two of them a good way, but had given it over. From thence they advanced to the first rising ground, where they had stood and seen their camp destroyed and where they had the mortification still to see some of the smoke: but neither could they here see any of the savages. They then resolved, though with all possible caution, to go forward, towards their ruined plantation; but a little before they came thither, coming in sight of the sea-shore, they saw plainly the savages all embarked again in their canoes, in order to be gone.

The poor Englishmen being now twice ruined, and all their improvements destroyed, the rest all agreed to come and help them to rebuild, and to assist them with needful supplies. Their three countrymen, who were not yet noted for having the least inclination to do any good, yet as soon as they heard of it (for they living remote eastward knew nothing of the matter till all was over), came and offered their help and assistance, and did very friendly work for several days, to restore their habitation, and make necessaries for them. And thus, in a little time, they were set upon their legs again.

It was five or six months after this before they heard any more of the savages, in which time our men were in hopes they had either forgot their former bad luck, or given over hopes of better; when, on a sudden, they were invaded with a most formidable fleet of no less than eight-and-twenty canoes full of savages, armed with bows and arrows, great clubs, wooden swords, and such-like engines of war; and they brought such numbers with them, that, in short, it put all our people into the utmost consternation.

These new invaders, leaving their canoes at the east end of the island, came ranging along the shore, directly towards the place, to the number of two hundred and fifty, as near as our men could judge. Our army was but small, indeed; but that which was worse, they had not arms for all their number neither. The whole account, it seems, stood thus: first, as to men, seventeen Spaniards, five Englishmen, old Friday, or Friday's father, the three slaves taken with the women, who proved very faithful, and three other slaves, who lived with the Spaniards. To arm these, they had eleven muskets, five pistols, three fowling-pieces, five muskets or fowling-pieces which were taken by me from the mutinous seamen whom I reduced, two swords, and three old halberds.

To their slaves they did not give either musket or fuse, but they had every one a halberd, or a long staff, like a quarter-staff, with a great spike of iron fastened into each end of it, and by his side a hatchet; also every one of our men had a hatchet. Two of the women could not be prevailed upon but they would come into the fight, and they had bows and arrows, which the Spaniards had taken from the savages when the first action happened, which I have spoken of, where the Indians fought with one another; and the women had hatchets too.

The Spaniard governor, whom I described so often, commanded the whole; and Will Atkins, who, though a dreadful fellow for wickedness, was a most daring, bold fellow, commanded under him. The savages came forward like lions; and our men, which was the worst of their fate, had no advantage in their situation; only that Will Atkins, who now proved a most useful fellow, with six men, was planted just behind a small thicket of bushes, as an advanced guard, with orders to let the first of them pass by, and then fire into the middle of them, and as soon as he had fired, to make his retreat as nimble as he could round a part of the wood, and so come in behind the Spaniards, where they stood, having a thicket of trees before them.

When the savages came on, they ran straggling about every way in heaps, out of all manner of order, and Will Atkins let about fifty of them pass by him; then seeing the rest come in a very thick throng he orders three of his men to fire, having loaded their muskets with six or seven bullets apiece, about as big as large pistol bullets. How many they killed or wounded they knew not, but the consternation and surprise was inexpressible among the savages; they were frightened to the last degree to hear such a dreadful noise, and see their men killed, and others hurt, but see nobody that did it; when, in the middle of their fright, Will Atkins and his other three let fly again among the thickest of them; and in less than a minute the first three being loaded again, gave them a third volley.

Had Will Atkins and his men retired immediately, as soon as they had fired, as they were ordered to do, or had the rest of the body been at hand, to have poured in their shot continually, the savages had been effectually routed; for the terror that was among them came principally from this, viz., that they were killed by the gods with thunder and lightning, and could see nobody that hurt them; but Will Atkins, staying to load again, discovered the cheat; some of the savages who were at a distance spying them, came upon them behind; and though Atkins and his men fired at them also, two or three times, and killed above twenty, retiring as fast as they could, yet they wounded Atkins himself, and killed one of his fellow Englishmen, with their arrows, as they did afterwards one Spaniard, and one of the Indian slaves who came with the women. This slave was a most gallant fellow, and fought most desperately, killing five of them with his own hand, having no weapon but one of the armed staves and a hatchet.

Our men being thus hard laid at, Atkins wounded and two other men killed, retreated to a rising ground in the wood; and the Spaniards, after firing three volleys upon them, retreated also; for their number was so great, and they were so desperate, that though above fifty of them were killed, and more than as many wounded, yet they came on in the teeth of our men, fearless of danger, and shot their arrows like a cloud; and it was observed that their wounded men, who were not quite disabled, were made outrageous by their wounds, and fought like madmen.

The Spaniard governor having drawn his little body up together upon a rising ground, Atkins, though he was wounded, would have had them march and charge again altogether at once, but the Spaniard replied: "Senhor Atkins, you see how their wounded men fight; let them alone till morning; all the wounded men will be stiff and sore with their wounds, and faint with the loss of blood: and so we shall have the fewer to engage." This advice was good; but Will Atkins replied merrily: "That is true, senhor, and so shall I too; and that is the reason I would go on while I am warm." "Well, Senhor Atkins," says the Spaniard, "you have behaved gallantly, and done your part; we will fight for you, if you cannot come on; but I think it best to stay till morning." So they waited.

But as it was a clear moonlight night, and they found the savages in great disorder about their dead and wounded men, and a great noise and hurry among them where they lay, they afterwards resolved to fall upon them in the night, especially if they could come to give them but one volley before they were discovered, which they had a fair opportunity to do; for one of the Englishmen, in whose quarter it was where the fight began, led them round between the woods and the seaside westward, and then turning short south, they came so near where the thickest of them lay, that, before they were seen or heard, eight of them fired in among them, and did dreadful execution upon them; in half a minute more, eight others fired after them, pouring in their small-shot in such quantity, that abundance were killed and wounded; and all this while they were not able to see who hurt them, or which way to fly.

The Spaniards charged again with the utmost expedition, and then divided themselves in three bodies, and resolved to fall in among them altogether. The savages stood altogether, but were in the utmost confusion, hearing the noise of our men shouting from three quarters together;

they would have fought if they had seen us; for as soon as we came near enough to be seen, some arrows were shot, and poor old Friday was wounded, though not dangerously; but our men gave them no time, but, running up to them, fired among them three ways, and then fell in with the butt-ends of their muskets, their swords, armed staves, and hatchets, and laid about them so well, that, in a word, they set up a dismal screaming and howling, flying to save their lives which way soever they could.

Our men were tired with the execution, and killed or mortally wounded in the two fights about one hundred and eighty of them; the rest being frightened out of their wits, scoured through the woods and over the hills, with all the speed, fear and nimble feet could help them to; and as we did not trouble ourselves much to pursue them, they got all together to the seaside where they landed, and where their canoes lay. But their disasters were not at an end yet; for it blew a terrible storm of wind that evening from the sea, so that it was impossible for them to go off; nay, the storm continuing all night, when the tide came up, their canoes were most of them driven by the surge of the sea so high upon the shore, that it required infinite toil to get them off; and some of them were even dashed to pieces against the beach, or against one another.

Our men, though glad of their victory, yet got little rest that night; but having refreshed themselves as well as they could, they resolved to march to that part of the island where the savages were fled, and see what posture they were in.

At length, they came in view of the place where the more miserable remains of the savages' army lay, where there appeared about a hundred still: their posture was generally sitting upon the ground, with their knees up towards their mouth, and the head put between the two hands, leaning down upon the knees.

The Spaniard governor ordered two muskets to be fired, without ball, to alarm them: this he did, that by their countenance he might know what to expect, viz., whether they were still in heart to fight, or were so heartily beaten as to be dispirited and discouraged, and so he might manage accordingly. This stratagem took; for as soon as the savages heard the first gun and saw the flash of the second, they started up upon their feet in the greatest consternation imaginable; and as our men advanced swiftly toward them, they all ran screaming and yelling away, with a kind of howling noise, which our men did not understand, and had never heard before: and thus they ran up the hills into the country.

At first our men had much rather the weather had been calm, and they had all gone away to sea; but Will Atkins, who, notwithstanding his wound, kept always with them, proved the best counsellor in this case: his advice was, to take the advantage that offered, and clap in between them and their boats, and so deprive them of the capacity of ever returning any more to plague the island.

Will Atkins told them they had better have to do with a hundred men than with a hundred nations; that as they must destroy their boats, so they must destroy the men, or be all of them destroyed themselves. In a word, he showed them the necessity of it so plainly, that they all came into it; so they went to work immediately with the boats, and getting some dry wood together from a dead tree, they tried to set some of them on fire, but they were so wet that they would not burn; however, the fire so burned the upper part, that it soon made them unfit for swimming in the sea as boats. When the Indians saw what they were about, some of them came running out of the woods, and coming as near as they could to our men, kneeled down and making pitiful gestures and strange noises, begged to have their boats spared, and that they would be gone, and never come there again. But our men were now satisfied that they had no way to preserve themselves or to save their colony, but effectually to prevent any of these people from ever going home again; so that, letting them know that they should not have any mercy, they fell to work with their canoes, and destroyed them every one that the storm had not destroyed before: at the sight of which the savages raised a hideous cry in the woods, which our people heard plain enough, after which they ran about the island like distracted men. Nor did the Spaniards, with all their prudence, consider that while they made those people thus desperate, they ought to have kept a good guard at the same time upon their plantations; for though, it is true, they had driven away their cattle, and the Indians did not find out their main retreat, I mean my old castle at the hill, nor the cave in the valley, yet they found out my plantation at the bower, and pulled it all to pieces, and all the fences and planting about it; trod all the corn under foot, tore up the vines and grapes, being just then almost ripe, and did our men an inestimable damage.

Though our men were able to fight them upon all occasions, yet they were in no condition to pursue them, or hunt them up and down; for as they were too nimble of foot for our men, when they found them single, so our men durst not go abroad single, for fear of being surrounded with their numbers. The best was, they had no weapons; for though they had bows, they had no arrows left, nor any materials to make any; nor had they any edge-tool or weapon among them.

When they saw what their circumstances were, the first thing they concluded was, that they would, if possible, drive them up to the farther part of the island, south-west, that if any more savages came on shore they might not find one another; then that they would daily hunt and harass them, and kill as many of them as they could come at, till they had reduced their number; and if they could at last tame them, and bring them to anything, they would give them corn, and teach them how to plant, and live upon their daily labour.

In order to do this, they so followed them, and so terrified them with their guns, that in a few days, if any of them fired a gun at an Indian, if he did not hit him, yet he would fall down for fear; and so dreadfully frightened they were, that they kept out of sight farther and farther; till, at last, our men following them, and almost every day killing or wounding some of them, they kept up in the woods or hollow places so much, that it reduced them to the utmost misery for want of food; and many were afterwards found dead in the woods, without any hurt, absolutely starved to death.

When our men found this, it made their hearts relent, and pity moved them, especially the Spaniard governor, who was the most gentleman-like, generous-minded man that I ever met with in my life; and he proposed, if possible, to take one of them alive, and bring him to understand what they meant, so far as to be able to act as interpreter, and go among them, and see if they might be brought to some conditions that might be depended upon, to save their lives and do us no harm.

It was some while before any of them could be taken; but being weak and half-starved, one of them was at last surprised and made a prisoner. They brought old Friday to him, who talked often with him, and told him how kind the others would be to them all; that they would not only save their lives, but would give them part of the island to live in, provided they would give satisfaction that they would keep in their own bounds, and not come beyond it to injure or prejudice others; and that they should have corn given them to plant and make it grow for their bread, and some bread given them for their present subsistence; and old Friday bade the fellow go and talk with the rest of his countrymen, and see what they said to it; assuring them, that if they did not agree immediately, they would be all destroyed.

The poor wretches thoroughly humbled, and reduced in number to about thirty-seven, closed with the proposal the first offer, and begged to have some food given them; upon which, twelve Spaniards and two Englishmen well armed, with three Indian slaves and old Friday, marched to the place where they were. The three Indian slaves carried them a large quantity of bread, some rice boiled up to cakes and dried in the sun, and three live goats; and they were ordered to go to the side of a hill, where they sat down, ate their provisions very thankfully, and were the most faithful fellows to their words that could be thought of; for, except when they came to beg victuals and directions, they never came out of their bounds; and there they lived when I came to the island, and I went to see them.

They had taught them both to plant corn, make bread, breed tame goats, and milk them; they wanted nothing but wives, and they soon would have been a nation. They were confined to a neck of land, surrounded with high rocks behind them, and lying plain towards the sea before them, on the south-east corner of the island. They had land enough, and it was very good and fruitful; about a mile and a half broad, and three or four miles in length.

Our men taught them to make wooden spades, such as I made for myself, and gave among them twelve hatchets, and three or four knives; and there they lived, the most subjected, innocent creatures that ever were heard of.

After this, the colony enjoyed a perfect tranquillity with respect to the savages, till I came to revisit them, which was about two years after; not but that, now and then, some canoes of savages came on shore for their triumphal, unnatural feasts; but as they were of several nations, and perhaps had never heard of those that came before, or the reason of it, they did not make any search or inquiry after their countrymen; and if they had, it would have been very hard to have found them out.

Thus, I think, I have given a full account of all that happened to them till my return, at least, that was worth notice. The Indians or savages were wonderfully civilised by them, and they frequently went among them; but forbade, on pain of death, any one of the Indians coming to them, because they would not have their settlement betrayed again. One thing was very remarkable, viz., that they taught the savages to make wicker-work or baskets, but they soon outdid their masters; for they made abundance of most ingenious things in wicker-work, particularly all sorts of baskets, sieves, bird-cages, cupboards, etc.; as also chairs to sit on, stools, beds, couches, and abundance of other things, being very ingenious at such work, when they were once put in the way of it.

SECTION XXXV

ROBINSON LEARNS FROM THE SPANIARDS THE DIFFICULTIES THEY HAD TO ENCOUNTER—HE FURNISHES THE PEOPLE WITH TOOLS, ETC.—THE FRENCH ECCLESIASTIC

HAVING thus given an account of the colony in general, I must say something of the Spaniards, who were the main body of the family, and in whose story there are some incidents also remarkable enough.

I had a great many discourses with them about their circumstances when they were among the savages. They told me readily that they had no instances to give of their application or ingenuity in that country; that they were a poor, miserable, and dejected handful of people; that if means had been put into their hands, yet they had so abandoned themselves to despair, and so sunk under the weight of their misfortunes, that they thought of nothing but starving. One of them, a grave sensible man, told me it was remarkable that Englishmen had a greater presence of mind, in their distress, than any people he ever met with; that their unhappy nation and the Portuguese were the worst men in the world to struggle with misfortunes for that their first step in dangers, after the common efforts were over, was to despair, lie down under it, and die, without rousing their thoughts up to proper remedies for their escape.

They gave me dismal accounts of the extremities they were driven to; how sometimes they were many days without food at all, the island they were upon being inhabited, by a sort of savages that lived more indolent, and for that reason were less supplied with the necessaries of life, than they had reason to believe others were in the same part of the world; and yet they found that these savages were less ravenous and voracious than those who had better supplies of food.

They then gave an account how the savages whom they lived among expected them to go out with them into their wars; but being without powder and shot, when they came into the field of battle, they were in a worse condition than the savages themselves; for they had neither bows nor arrows, nor could they use those the savages gave them; so they could do nothing but stand still, and be wounded with arrows, till they came up to the teeth of their enemy; till at last they found the way to make themselves large targets of wood, which they covered with skins of wild beasts, whose names they knew not, and these covered them from the arrows of the savages; yet notwithstanding these, they were sometimes in great danger; and five of them were once knocked down together with the clubs of the savages, which was the time when one of them was taken prisoner, that is to say, the Spaniard whom I had relieved: that at first they thought had been killed; but when they afterwards heard he was taken prisoner, they were under the greatest grief imaginable, and would willingly have all ventured their lives to have rescued him.

They described most affectionately how they were surprised with joy at the return of their friend and companion in misery, who, they thought, had been devoured by wild beasts of the worst kind, viz., by wild men; and yet how much more they were surprised with the account he gave them of his errand, and that there was a Christian in any place near, much more one that was able, and had humanity enough, to contribute to their deliverance.

They described how they were astonished at the sight of the relief I sent them, and at the appearance of loaves of bread, things they had not seen since their coming to that miserable place; and, after all, they would have told me something of the joy they were in at the sight of a boat and pilots, to carry them away to the person and place from whence all these new comforts came, but it was impossible to express it by words, for their excessive joy naturally driving them to unbecoming extravagances, they had no way to describe them, but by telling me they bordered upon lunacy. All these things made me more sensible of the relation of these poor men, and more affected with it. Then I entered into a serious discourse with the Spaniard, whom I call governor, about their stay in the island. I told them I came to establish them there, not to remove them: and then I let them know that I had brought with me relief of sundry kinds for them; that I had been at a great charge to supply them with all things necessary, as well for their convenience as their defence; and that I had such and such particular persons with me, as well to increase and recruit their number, as by the particular necessary employments which they were bred to, being artificers, to assist them in those things in which they were at present in want.

They were altogether when I talked thus to them: and before I delivered to them the stores I had brought, I asked them, one by one, if they had entirely forgot and buried the first animosities that had been among them, and would shake hands with one another, and engage in a strict friendship and union of interest, that so there might be no more misunderstandings and jealousies.

Will Atkins, with abundance of frankness and good humour, said, they had met with affliction enough to make them all sober, and enemies enough to make them all friends; that, for his part, he was very willing and desirous of living in terms of entire friendship and union with them, and would do anything that lay in his power to convince them of it: and as for going to England, he cared not if he did not go thither these twenty years.

The Spaniards said they had, indeed, at first disarmed and excluded Will Atkins and his two countrymen for their ill conduct; but that Will Atkins had behaved himself so bravely in the great fight they had with the savages, and on several occasions since, and had showed himself so faithful to, and concerned for, the general interest of them all, that they had forgotten all that was past, and thought he merited as much to be trusted with arms, and supplied with necessaries, as any of them: and they had testified their satisfaction in him, by committing the command to him, next to the governor himself; and as they had entire confidence in him, and all his countrymen, so they acknowledged they had merited that confidence by all the methods that honest men could merit to be valued and trusted; and they most heartily embraced the occasion of giving me this assurance, that they would never have any interest separate from one another.

Upon these frank and open declarations of friendship we appointed the next day to dine all together; and, indeed, we made a splendid feast.

After this feast, at which we were very innocently merry, I brought out my cargo of goods: wherein that there might be no dispute about dividing, I showed them that there was a sufficiency for them all.

Then, having distributed the goods among them, I presented to them the people I had brought with me, particularly the tailor, the smith, and the two carpenters, all of them most necessary people; but, above all, my general artificer, than whom they could not name anything that was more useful to them: and the tailor, to show his concern for them, went to work immediately, and, with my leave, made them every one a shirt, the first thing he did; and, which was still more, he taught the women not only how to sew and stitch, and use the needle, but made them assist to make the shirts for their husbands and for all the rest.

Then I brought them out all my store of tools, and gave

every man a digging-spade, shovel, and rake, for we had no harrows or ploughs; and to every separate place a pick-axe a crow, a broad-axe, and a saw; always appointing that as often as any were broken or worn out, they should be supplied without grudging, out of the general stores that I left behind. Nails, staples, hinges, hammers, chiseis, knives, scissors, and all sorts of iron work, they had without tale, as they required; and for the use of the smith, I left two tons of unwrought iron for a supply.

My magazine of powder and arms which I brought them was such, even to profusion, that they could not but rejoice at them; for now they could march as I used to do, with a musket upon each shoulder, if there was occasion; and were able to fight a thousand savages, if they had but some little advantages of situation, which also they could not miss, if they had occasion.

I carried on shore with me the young man whose mother was starved to death, and the maid also; she was a sober, well-educated, religious young woman, and behaved so inoffensively, that every one gave her a good word. After a while, seeing things so well ordered, and in so fine a way of thriving upon my island, and considering that they had neither business nor acquaintance in the East Indies, or reason for making so long a voyage; both of them desired I would give them leave to remain on the island, and be entered among the family, as they called it. I agreed to this readily; and they had a little plot of ground allotted to them, where they had three tents or houses set up, surrounded with a basket-work, pallisadoed like Atkins', adjoining to his plantation. And now the other two Englishmen removed their habitation to the same place; and so the island was divided into three colonies, and no more, viz., the Spaniards, with old Friday, and the first servants, at my old habitation under the hill, which was, in a word, the capital city; and where they had so enlarged and extended their works, as well under as on the outside of the hill, that they lived, though perfectly concealed, yet full at large. Never was there such a little city in a wood, and so hid, in any part of the world.

The other colony was that of Will Atkins, where there were four families of Englishmen, I mean those I had left there, with their wives and children; three savages that were slaves; the widow and the children of the Englishman that was killed; the young man and the maid; and, by the way, we made a wife of her before we went away. There were also the two carpenters and the tailor, whom I brought with me for them; also the smith, who was a very necessary man to them, especially as a gunsmith, to take care of their arms; and my other man, whom I called Jack-of-all-trades, who was in himself as good almost as twenty men; for he was not only a very ingenious fellow, but a very merry fellow; and before I went away the French ecclesiastic that I had brought with me married him to the honest maid that came with the youth in the ship I mentioned before.

Having now done with the island, I left them all in good circumstances, and in a flourishing condition, and went on board my ship again on the 6th of May, having been about twenty-five days among them.

SECTION XXXVI

ENCOUNTER WITH SAVAGES AT SEA—FRIDAY'S DEATH—ROBINSON FINDS HIS FORMER PARTNER IN THE BRAZILS—SAILS FOR THE EAST INDIES

THE next day, giving them a salute of five guns at parting, we set sail, and arrived at the Bay of All Saints, in the Brazils, in about twenty-two days, meeting nothing remarkable in our passage but this. The third day, towards evening, the sea smooth, and the weather calm, we saw the sea, as it were, covered towards the land with something very black. Our chief mate, going up the mainshrouds a little way, and looking at them with a perspective, cried out it was an army. I could not imagine what he meant by an army, and thwarted him a little hastily. "Nay, sir," says he, "don't be angry, for 'tis an army, and a fleet too; for I believe there are a thousand canoes, and you may see them paddle along, for they are coming towards us apace."

I was a little surprised, then, indeed, and so was my nephew the captain; for he had heard such terrible stories of them in the island, and having never been in those seas before, that he could not tell what to think of it, but said, two or three times, we should all be devoured. I must confess, considering we were becalmed, and the current set strong towards the shore, I liked it the worse; however, I bade them not be afraid, but bring the ship to an anchor as soon as we came so near as to know that we must engage them.

The weather continued calm, and they came on apace towards us; so I gave orders to come to an anchor, and furl all our sails: as for the savages, I told them they had nothing to fear but fire, and therefore they should get their boats out, and fasten them, one close by the head, and the other by the stern, and man them both well, and wait the issue in that posture; this I did, that the men in the boats might be ready with sheets and buckets to put out any fire these savages would endeavour to fix to the outside of the ship.

In this posture we lay by for them, and in a little while they came up with us; but never was such a horrid sight seen by Christians: though my mate was much mistaken in his calculation of their number, yet when they came up we reckoned about a hundred and twenty-six canoes; some of them had sixteen or seventeen men in them, some more, and the least six or seven.

When they came nearer to us, they seemed to be struck with wonder and astonishment, as at a sight which doubtless they had never seen before; nor could they, at first, as we afterwards understood, know what to make of us; they came boldly up, however, very near to us, and seemed to go about to row round us; but we called to our men in the boats not to let them come too near them. This very order brought us to an engagement with them, without our designing it; for five or six of the large canoes came so near our long-boat that our men beckoned with their hands to keep them back, which they understood very well, and went back, but at their retreat about fifty arrows came on board us from those boats, and one of our men in the long-boat was very much wounded. However, I called to them not to fire by any means; but we handed down some deal boards into the boat, and the carpenter presently set up a kind of fence, like waste boards, to cover them from the arrows of the savages, if they should shoot again.

About half an hour afterwards they all came up in a body astern of us, and so near, as that we could easily discern what they were, though we could not tell their design; and I easily found they were some of my old friends, the same sort of savages that I had been used to engage with; and in a short time more they rowed a little farther out to sea, till they came so near that they could hear us speak: upon this I ordered all my men to keep close, lest they should shoot any more arrows, and made all our guns ready; but being so near as to be within hearing, I made Friday go out upon the deck, and call out aloud to them in his language, to know what they meant; which, accordingly he did. Immediately afterwards, Friday cried out they were going to shoot, and, unhappily for him, poor fellow, they let fly about three hundred of their arrows, and, to my inexpressible grief, killed poor Friday, no other man being in their sight. The poor fellow was shot with no less than three arrows, and about three more fell very near him; such unlucky marksmen they were!

I was so enraged at the loss of my old trusty servant and companion, that I immediately ordered five guns to be loaded with small shot, and four with great, and gave them such a broadside as they had never heard in their lives before, to be sure. They were not above half a cable length off when we fired; and our gunners took their aim so well that three or four of their canoes were overset, as we had reason to believe, by one shot only.

I can neither tell how many we killed, nor how many we wounded, at this broadside, but sure such a fright and hurry never was seen among such a multitude; there were thirteen or fourteen of their canoes split and overset in all, and the men all set a-swimming; the rest, frightened out of their wits, scoured away as fast as they could, taking but little care to save those whose boats were split or spoiled with our shot; so I suppose that many of them were lost; and our men took up one poor fellow swimming for his life, above an hour after they were all gone.

We had a prisoner, indeed, but the creature was so sullen that he would neither eat nor speak, and we all fancied he would starve himself to death; but I took a way to cure him; for I made them turn him into the long-boat and made him believe they would toss him into the sea again, and so leave him where they found him, if he would not speak; nor would that do, but they really did throw him into the sea, and came away from him, and then he followed them, for he swam like a cork, and called in his tongue, though they understood not one word of what he said; however, at last they took him in again, and then he began to be more tractable; nor did I ever design they should drown him.

We were now under sail again; but I was the most disconsolate creature alive for want of my man Friday.

And now I name the poor fellow once more, I must take my last leave of him; poor honest Friday! We buried him with all the decency and solemnity possible, by putting him into a coffin, and throwing him into the sea; and I caused them to fire eleven guns for him; and so ended the life of the most grateful, faithful, honest, and most affectionate servant that ever man had.

We went now away with a fair wind for Brazil; and in about twelve days' time we made land, in the latitude of five degrees south of the line, being the north-easternmost land on all that part of America. We kept on S. by E. in sight of the shore four days, when we made Cape St. Augustine, and in three days came to an anchor off the Bay of All Saints, the old place of my deliverance, from whence came both my good and evil fate.

Never ship came to this port that had less business than I had, and yet it was with great difficulty that we were admitted to have the least correspondence on shore; nor my partner himself, who was alive, and made a great figure among them, not my two merchant trustees, not the fame of my wonderful preservation in the island, could obtain me that favour; but my partner, remembering that I had given five hundred moidores to the priory of the monastery of the Augustines, and two hundred and seventy-two to the poor, went to the monastery, and obliged the prior that then was, to go to the governor, and get leave for me personally, with the captain and one more, besides eight seamen, to come on shore, and no more; and this upon condition absolutely capitulated for, that we should not offer to land any goods out of the ship, or to carry any person away without licence. They were so strict with us as to landing any goods, that it was with extreme difficulty that I got on shore three bales of English goods, such as fine broadcloths, stuffs, and some linen, which I had brought for a present to my partner.

He was a very generous, open-hearted man; though, like me, he came from little at first; and though he knew not that I had the least design of giving him anything, he sent me on board a present of fresh provisions, wine, and sweetmeats, worth about thirty moidores, including some tobacco, and three or four fine medals of gold; but I was even with him in my present, which, as I have said, consisted of fine broadcloth, English stuffs, lace, and fine hollands; also, I delivered him about the value of one hundred pounds sterling, in the same goods, for other uses; and I obliged him to set up the sloop, which I had brought with me from England, as I have said, for the use of my colony, in order to send the refreshments I intended to my plantation.

Accordingly, he got hands, and finished the sloop in a very few days, for she was already framed; and I gave the master of her such instructions as that he could not miss the place; nor did he, as I had an account from my partner afterwards. I got him soon loaded with the small cargo I sent them; and one of our seamen, that had been on shore with me there, offered to go with the sloop and settle there, upon my letter to the governor Spaniard to allot him a sufficient quantity of land for a plantation.

The cargo arrived safe, and, as you may easily suppose, was very welcome to my old inhabitants, who were now, with this addition, between sixty and seventy people, besides little children, of which there were a great many. I found letters at London from them all, by way of Lisbon, when I came back to England, of which I shall also take some notice immediately.

I have now done with the island, and all manner of discourse about it; and whoever reads the rest of my memorandums would do well to turn his thoughts entirely from it, and expect to read of the follies of an old man, not warned by his own harms, much less by those of other men, to beware of the like; not cooled by almost forty years' miseries and disappointments; not satisfied with prosperity beyond expectation, nor made cautious by afflictions and distress beyond imitation.

From the Brazils we made directly over the Atlantic

Sea to the Cape of Good Hope, and had a tolerably good voyage, our course generally south-east, now and then a storm and some contrary winds, but my disasters at sea were at an end, my future rubs and cross events were to befall me on shore.

SECTION XXXVII

THE VESSEL TOUCHES AT MADAGASCAR—AFFRAY WITH THE NATIVES—WHO ARE MASSACRED BY THE CREW—THE SAILORS REFUSE TO SAIL WITH ROBINSON, WHO IS LEFT BY HIS NEPHEW, THE CAPTAIN, IN BENGAL

WE stayed at the Cape no longer than was needful to take in fresh water, but made the best of our way for the coast of Coromandel. We touched first at the island of Madagascar, where, though the people are fierce and treacherous, and very well armed with lances and bows, which they use with inconceivable dexterity, yet we fared very well with them a while; but a party of our sailors, being ashore, were by the boatswain involved in a quarrel with the Indians, wherein one of our men was killed with a lance that was thrown at him. Incited by the boatswain, our fellows the same night did surprise and fire the village, butchering the poor Indians, men and women alike, very horridly. I was very angry with my nephew, the captain, as prompting rather than cooling the rage of his men in so bloody and cruel an enterprise.

We were now bound to the Gulf of Persia, and from thence to the coast of Coromandel, only to touch at Surat; but the chief of the supercargo's design lay at the Bay of Bengal; where if he missed his business outward-bound, he was to go up to China, and return to the coast as he came home.

The first disaster that befell us was in the Gulf of Persia, where five of our men venturing on shore on the Arabian side of the gulf, were surrounded by the Arabians, and either all killed or carried away into slavery; the rest of the boat's crew were not able to rescue them, and had but just time to get off their boat. I began to upbraid them with the just retribution of Heaven in this case for cruelty they had exercised on the natives of Madagascar.

But my frequent preaching to them on the subject had worse consequences than I expected; and the boatswain, who had been the head of the attempt, came up boldly to me one time, and told me that, unless I would resolve to have done with it, and also not to concern myself any further with him, or any of his affairs, he would leave the ship; for he did not think it was safe to sail with me among them.

I then told him, that I was a considerable owner in the ship; in that claim, I conceived I had a right to speak even further than I had done, and would not be accountable to him or any one else. He made but little reply to me at that time, and I thought the affair had been over. We were at this time in the road at Bengal; and being willing to see the place, I went on shore with the supercargo, in the ship's boat, to divert myself; and towards evening was preparing to go on board, when one of the men came to me, and told me he would not have me trouble myself to come down to the boat, for they had orders not to carry me on board any more.

I immediately went and found out the supercargo, and told him the story; adding, what I presently foresaw, that there would be a mutiny in the ship; and entreated him to go immediately on board the ship in an Indian boat, and acquaint the captain of it. But I might have spared this intelligence, for before I had spoken to him on shore the matter was effected on board. The boatswain, the gunner, the carpenter, and all the inferior officers, as soon as I was gone off in the boat, came up, and desired to speak with the captain; and there the boatswain told the captain, in a few words, that as I was now going peaceably on shore they were loth to use any violence with me, which, if I had not gone on shore, they would otherwise have done, to oblige me to have gone; they therefore thought fit to tell him, that as they shipped themselves to serve in the ship under his command, they would perform it well and faithfully; but if I would not quit the ship, or the captain oblige me to quit it, they would all leave the ship—and sail no farther with him.

When my nephew told me what they had said to him I told him he should not be concerned at it at all, for I would stay on shore; I only desired he would send all my necessary things on shore, and leave me a sufficient sum of money, and I would find my way to England as well as I could.

So that the matter was over in a few hours, the men returned to their duty, and I began to consider what course I should steer.

SECTION XXXVIII

MEETS WITH AN ENGLISH MERCHANT WITH WHOM HE MAKES SOME TRADING VOYAGES—THEY ARE MISTAKEN FOR PIRATES—VANQUISH THEIR PURSUERS—VOYAGE TO CHINA—GULF OF NANQUIN—APPREHENSIONS OF FALLING INTO THE HANDS OF THE DUTCH

I WAS now alone in the most remote part of the world, as I think I may call it, for I was near three thousand leagues by sea farther off from England than I was at my island; only, it is true, I might travel here by land over the great Mogul's country to Surat, might go from thence to Bassora by sea, up the Gulf of Persia, and take the way of the caravans, over the Desert of Arabia, to Aleppo and Scanderoon; from thence by sea again to Italy, and so overland into France; and this put together might at least be a full diameter of the globe, or more.

Here I had the mortification to see the ship set sail without me; a treatment I think a man in my circumstances scarce ever met with, except from pirates running away with the ship, and setting those that would not agree with their villainy on shore. However, my nephew left me two servants, or rather one companion and one servant; the first was clerk to the purser, whom he engaged to go with me, and the other was his own servant. I took me also a good lodging in the house of an Englishwoman, where several merchants lodged, some French, two Italians, or rather Jews, and one Englishman.

After a long stay here, the English merchant who lodged with me, and whom I had contracted an intimate acquaintance with, came to me one morning. "Countryman," says he, "I have a project to communicate to you, which, as it suits with my thoughts, may, for aught I know, suit with yours also, when you shall have thoroughly considered it. If you will put one thousand pounds to my one thousand pounds, we will hire a ship here, the first we can get to our minds; you shall be captain, I'll be merchant, and we'll go a trading voyage to China."

I liked this proposal very well, and the more because it seemed to be expressed with so much goodwill, and in so friendly a manner.

It was, however, some time before we could get a ship to our minds, and when we had got a vessel, it was not easy to get English sailors; that is to say, so many as were necessary to govern the voyage and manage the sailors which we should pick up there. After some time we got a mate, a boatswain, and a gunner, English; a Dutch carpenter, and three foremastmen. With these we found we could do well enough, having Indian seamen, such as they were, to make up.

We made this voyage to Achin, in the island of Sumatra, and from thence to Siam, where we exchanged some of our wares for opium and some arrack; the first a commodity which bears a great price among the Chinese, and which at that time, was much wanted there. In a word, we went up to Suskan, made a very great voyage, were eight months out, and returned to Bengal; and I was very well satisfied with my adventure.

In short, we made a very good voyage, and I got so much money by my first adventure, and such an insight into the method of getting more, that, had I been twenty years younger, I should have been tempted to have stayed here, and sought no farther for making any fortune: but what was all this to a man upwards of threescore, that was rich enough, and came abroad more in obedience to a restless desire of seeing the world than covetous desire of gaining by it?

But this was not all: I had a kind of impatience upon me to be nearer home, and yet the most unsettled resolution imaginable which way to go. In the interval of these consultations, my friend, who was always upon the search for business, proposed another voyage to me among the Spice Islands, and to bring home a loading of cloves from the Manillas, or thereabouts.

We were not long in preparing for this voyage, which we

made very successfully, touching at Borneo, and several islands whose names I do not remember, and came home in about five months. We sold our spice, which was chiefly cloves and some nutmegs, to the Persian merchants, who carried them away to the gulf; and making near five of one, we really got a great deal of money.

But, to be short with my speculations, a little while after this there came in a Dutch ship from Batavia; she was a coaster, of about two hundred tons burthen; the men, as they pretended, having been so sickly, that the captain had not hands enough to go to sea with, he lay by at Bengal, and gave public notice that he would sell his ship. This came to my ears before my new partner heard of it, and I had a great mind to buy it; so I went to him and told him of it. He considered awhile, for he was no rash man; but musing some time, he replied: "She is a little too big; but, however, we will have her." Accordingly, we bought the ship, and, agreeing with the master, we paid for her, and took possession. When we had done so, we resolved to entertain the men, if we could, to join them with those we had for the pursuing our business; but on a sudden, they having received not their wages, but their share of the money, as we afterwards learned, not one of them was to be found.

A few days after, I came to know what sort of fellows they were; for, in short, their history was, that this man they called captain was the gunner only, not the commander; that they had been a trading voyage, in which they had been attacked on shore by some of the Malays, who had killed the captain and three of his men; and that, after the captain was killed, these men, eleven in number, had resolved to run away with the ship, which they did, and brought her to Bengal, leaving the mate and five more men on shore.

We picked up some more English sailors here after this, and some Dutch; and now we resolved for a second voyage to the south-east for cloves, etc., that is to say, among the Philippine and Molucca isles; and, in short, not to fill up this part of my story with trifles, when what is to come is so remarkable, I spent, from first to last, six years in this country, trading from port to port, backward and forward, with very great success, and was now the last year with my new partner, going in the ship above mentioned on a voyage to China, but designing first to go to Siam, to buy rice.

In this voyage, being by contrary winds obliged to beat up and down a great while in the straits of Malacca, and among the islands, we were no sooner got clear of those difficult seas than we found our ship had sprung a leak, and we were not able by all our industry, to find out where it was. This forced us to make some port; and my partner, who knew the country better than I did, directed the captain to put into the river Cambodia; for I had made the English mate, one Mr. Thompson, captain, not being willing to take the charge of the ship upon myself. While we were here and going often on shore for refreshment, there comes to me one day an Englishman, and he was, it seems, a gunner's mate on board an English East India ship which rode in the same river. "Sir," says he, "you are a stranger to me, and I to you, but I have something to tell you that very nearly concerns you." "If it very nearly concerns me," said I, "and not yourself, what moves you to tell it to me?" "I am moved," says he, "by the imminent danger you are in, and, for aught I see, you have no knowledge of it." "I know no danger I am in," says I, "but that my ship is leaky, and I cannot find it out; but I intend to lay her aground to-morrow to see if I can find it." "But, sir," says he, "leaky or not leaky, find it or not find it, you will be wiser than to lay your ship on shore to-morrow, when you hear what I have to say to you. Do you know, sir," said he, "the town of Cambodia lies about fifteen leagues up this river? and there are two large English ships about five leagues on this side, and three Dutch?" "Well," said I, "and what is that to me?" "Well, sir," says he, "if you do not put to sea immediately, you will the very next tide be attacked by five long-boats full of men, and, perhaps, if you are taken, you will be hanged for a pirate, and the particulars be examined afterwards. I suppose, you know well enough, viz., that you was with this ship at Sumatra; that there your captain was murdered by the Malays, with three of his men; and that you, or some of those that were on board with you, ran away with the ship, and are since turned pirates. This is the sum of the story, and you will all be seized as pirates, I can assure you, and executed with very little ceremony; for you know merchant ships show but little law to pirates, if they get them into their power; if you have any regard for your life, and the lives of all your men, put to sea without fail, at high water." "Well," said I, "you have been very kind in this; what shall I do to make amends?" "Sir," says he, "I will make an offer to you; I have nineteen months' pay due to me on board the ship which I came out of England in; and the Dutchman that is with me has seven months' pay due to him; if you will make good our pay to us, we will go along with you: if you find nothing more in it, we will desire no more; but if we do convince you that we have saved your lives, and the ship, and the lives of all the men in her, we will leave the rest to you."

I consented to this readily, and went immediately on board, and the two men with me. As soon as I came to the ship's side, my partner, who was on board, came out on the quarter-deck and called to me, with a great deal of joy. "O ho! O ho! we have stopped the leak! we have stopped the leak!" "Say you so?" said I, "thank God; but weigh anchor then immediately." "He was surprised, but, however, he called the captain, and he immediately ordered the anchor to be got up; and though the tide was not quite down, we stood out to sea. Then I called him into the cabin, and told him the story. Presently a seaman comes to the cabin door, and called out to us that the captain bade him tell us we were chased. "Chased!" says I; "by what?" "By five sloops, or boats," says the fellow, "full of men." We made ready for fight: but all this while we kept out to sea, with wind enough, and could see the boats at a distance, being five large long-boats following us with all the sail they could make.

Two of these boats (which by our glasses we could see were English) outsailed the rest, were near two leagues ahead of them and gained upon us considerably, so that we found they would come up with us; upon which we fired a gun without ball, to intimate that they should bring to; and we put out a flag of truce, as a signal for parley, but they came crowding after us, till they came within shot, when we took in our white flag, they having made answer to it, and hung out a red flag, and fired at them with shot. Notwithstanding this, they came on till they were near enough to call to them with a speaking-trumpet which we had on board; so we called to them, and bade them keep off, at their peril.

It was all one: they crowded after us, and endeavoured to come under our stern, so as to board us on our quarter; upon which, seeing they were resolute for mischief, and depended upon the strength that followed them, I ordered to bring the ship to, so that they lay upon our broadside; when immediately we fired our guns at them, one of which had been levelled so true as to carry away the stern of the hindermost boat, and bring them to the necessity of taking down their sail, and running all to the head of the boat to keep her from sinking. While this was doing, one of the three boats that was behind, being forwarder than the other two, made up to the boat which we had disabled, to relieve her, and we could see her take out the men; we called again to the foremost boat and offered a truce but had no answer, only she crowded close under our stern. Upon this our gunner, who was a very dexterous fellow, ran out his two chase guns, and fired again at her. Then we wore the ship again, and brought our quarter to bear upon them, and firing three guns more, we found the boat was almost split to pieces; in particular, her rudder and a piece of her stern were shot quite away. We found the boat sinking, and some of the men already in the water: upon this I immediately manned out our pinnace, which we had kept close by our side, with orders to pick up some of the men. Our men in the pinnace followed their orders, and took up three men, one of whom was just drowning, and it was a good while before we could recover him. As soon as they were on board, we crowded all the sail we could make, and stood farther out to sea; and we found that when the other three boats came up to the first they gave over their chase.

Being thus delivered from a danger I resolved that we should change our course and not let any one know whither we were going: so we stood out to sea, eastward, quite out of the course of all European ships.

When we were at sea, we began to consult with the two seamen, and inquire what the meaning of all this could be; and the Dutchman let us into the secret at once, telling us that the fellow that sold us the ship, as we said, was no more than a thief that had run away with her. Then he told us how the captain was treacherously murdered by the natives on the coast of Malacca, with three of his men; and that he, this Dutchman, and four more, got into the woods, where they wandered about a great while, till at length he, in particular, in a miraculous manner, made his escape, and swam off to a Dutch ship.

He then told us that he went to Batavia, where two of the seamen belonging to the ship arrived, having deserted the rest in their travels, and gave an account that the fellow who had run away with the ship sold her at Bengal to a set of pirates, which were gone a-cruising in her.

It was my partner's opinion we should go directly back to Bengal, from whence we came, because there we could give a good account of ourselves, could prove where we were when the ship put in, of whom we bought her, and the like.

I was some time of my partner's opinion; but after a little more serious thinking, I told him I thought it was a very great hazard for us to attempt returning to Bengal, for that we should be sure to be waylaid. This danger a little startled my partner, and all the ship's company, and we immediately resolved to go to Nanquin.

We sailed directly for Nanquin, and in time came to an anchor at the south-west point of the great Gulf of Nanquin; where, by the way, I came by accident to understand that two Dutch ships were gone that length before me, and that I should certainly fall into their hands. I asked the old pilot if there was no creek or harbour which I might put into and pursue my business with the Chinese privately, and be in no danger of the enemy. He told me, if I would sail to the southward about forty-two leagues, there was a little port called Quinchang, where the fathers of the mission usually landed from Macao, on their progress to teach the Christian religion to the Chinese, and where no European ships ever put in.

We all agreed to go back to this place and we weighed the next day, having only gone twice on shore where we were to get fresh water.

We came to the other port (the wind being contrary) not till five days, but it was very much to our satisfaction; and I was joyful and I may say thankful, when I set my foot on shore, resolving, and my partner too, that if it was possible to dispose of ourselves and effects any other way, though not every way to our satisfaction, we would never set one foot on board that unhappy vessel more.

A French priest, Father Simon, was appointed, it seems, by order of the chief of the mission to go up to Pekin, the royal seat of the Chinese emperor, and waited only for another priest, who was ordered to come to him from Macao, to go along with him; and we scarce ever met together but he was inviting me to go that journey; telling me how he would show me all the glorious things of that mighty empire, and, among the rest, the greatest city in the world: "a city," said he, "that your London and our Paris put together cannot be equal to." This was the city of Pekin, which, I confess is very great.

We had something else before us at first, for we had all this while our ship and our merchandise to dispose of. Providence began here to clear up our way a little; and the first thing that offered was, that our old Portuguese pilot brought a Japan merchant to us, who bought all our opium and gave us a very good price for it. While we were dealing with him for our opium, it came into my head that he might perhaps deal for the ship too, and I ordered the interpreter to propose it to him; he shrugged up his shoulders at it when it was first proposed to him; but in a few days after he came to me, with one of the missionary priests for his interpreter, and told me he had a proposal to make to me, which was this: if I would let the same men who were in the ship navigate her, he would send them from thence to the Philippine islands with another loading, which he would pay the freight of before they went to Japan, and that at their return he would buy the ship. We accepted his proposal.

My partner and I discoursed the position of the young man whom my nephew had left with me as a companion, and my partner made a most generous offer. "You know it has been an unlucky ship," said he, "and we both resolve not to go to sea in it again: if your steward (so he called my man) will venture the voyage, I will leave my share of the vessel to him, and let him make the best of it; and if we live to meet in England, and he meets with success abroad, he shall account for one half of the profits of the ship's freight to us, the other shall be his own."

If my partner, who was no way concerned with my young man, made him such an offer, I could not do less than offer him the same: and all the ship's company being willing to go with him, we made over half the ship to him in property, and took a writing from him obliging him to account for the other: and away he went to Japan.

SECTION XXXIX

JOURNEY TO PEKIN—ROBINSON JOINS A CARAVAN PROCEEDING TO MOSCOW—RENCONTRES WITH THE TARTARS

I WAS now as near as I can compute, in the heart of China, about thirty degrees north of the line. I had, indeed, a mind to see the city of Pekin, which I had heard so much of, and Father Simon importuned me daily to do it.

We were twenty-five days travelling to Pekin, through a country infinitely populous, but I think badly cultivated; the husbandry, the economy, and the way of living miserable, though they boast so much of the industry of the people: I say miserable if compared with our own, but not so to these poor wretches, who know no other. The pride of the people is infinitely great, and exceeded by nothing but their poverty; which adds to that which I call their misery.

At length we arrived at Pekin; I had nobody with me but the youth whom my nephew the captain had given me to attend me as a servant, and who proved very trusty and diligent; and my partner had nobody with him, but one servant, who was a kinsman. As for the Portuguese pilot, he being desirous to see the court we bore his charges for his company, and to use him as an interpreter, for he understood the language of the country, and spoke good French and a little English; and, indeed, this old man was a most useful implement to us everywhere; for we had not been above a week at Pekin when he came and told us there was a great caravan of Muscovite and Polish merchants in the city, preparing to set out on their journey by land to Muscovy, within four or five weeks, and he was sure we would take the opportunity to go with them, and leave him behind to go back alone.

We then went to consult together what was to be done; and I and my partner agreed that if our Portuguese pilot would go with us we would bear his charges to Moscow or to England if he pleased. He received the proposal like a man transported, and told us he would go with us over the whole world.

It was in the beginning of February, our style, when we set out from Pekin.

The company was very great, and, as near as I can remember, made between three and four hundred horses, and upwards of one hundred and twenty men, very well armed, and provided for all events: for as the Eastern caravans are subject to be attacked by the Arabs, so are these by the Tartars; but they are not altogether so dangerous as the Arabs, nor so barbarous when they prevail.

In two days more we passed the great China wall, made for a fortification against the Tartars; and a very great work it is, going over hills and mountains in a needless track, where the rocks are impassable, and the precipices such as no enemy could possibly enter, or indeed climb up, or where, if they did, no wall could hinder them. They tell us its length is near a thousand English miles, but that the country is five hundred in a straight measured line, which the wall bounds, without measuring the windings and turnings it takes: it is about four fathoms high, and as many thick in some places.

And here I began to find the necessity of keeping together in a caravan as we travelled, for we saw several troops of Tartars roving about. Our leader for the day gave leave for about sixteen of us to go a-hunting, as they call it, and what was this but hunting of sheep; however, it may be called hunting too, for the creatures are the wildest and swiftest of foot that ever I saw of their kind; only they will not run a great way, and you are sure of sport when you begin the chase, for they appear generally thirty or forty in a flock, and, like true sheep, always keep together when they fly.

We were all this while in the Chinese dominions, and therefore the Tartars were not so bold as afterwards; but in about five days we entered a vast, great wild desert, which held us three days and nights' march; and we were obliged to carry our water with us in great leathern bottles, and to encamp all night, just as I have heard they do in the desert of Arabia.

I asked our guides whose dominion this was in; and they told me this was a kind of border, and might be called No Man's Land, being a part of Great Karakathay or Grand Tartary; but, however, it was all reckoned as belonging to China, but that there was no care taken here to preserve it from the inroads of thieves, and therefore it was reckoned the worst desert in the whole march, though we were to go over some much larger.

In passing this wilderness, which was at first very frightful to me, we saw two or three times, little parties of the Tartars. Once a party of them came so near as to stand and gaze at us; whether it was to consider if they should attack us or not, we knew not, but when we were passed at some distance by them we made a rearguard of forty men, and stood ready for them, letting the caravan pass half a mile or thereabouts before us: but after a while they marched off; only we found they saluted us with five arrows at their parting, one of which wounded a horse so that it disabled him, and we left him the next day, poor creature, in great need of a good farrier; they might shoot more arrows which might fall short of us, but we saw no more arrows or Tartars that time.

We travelled near a month after this, the ways not being so good as at first, though still in the dominions of the emperor of China, but lay for the most part in villages, some of which were fortified because of the incursions of the Tartars.

We wanted above two days' journey of the city of Naum when messengers were sent express to every part of the road to tell all travellers and caravans to halt till they had a guard sent for them; for that an unusual body of Tartars, making ten thousand in all, had appeared in the way, about thirty miles beyond the city.

Accordingly, two days after we had two hundred soldiers sent us from a garrison of the Chinese, on our left, and three hundred more from the city of Naum, and with these we advanced boldly. About three hours after, when we were entered upon a desert of about fifteen or sixteen miles over, behold, by a cloud of dust they raised, we saw an enemy was at hand; and they were at hand, indeed, for they came on upon the spur.

The Tartars came on and an innumerable company they were: how many we could not tell, but ten thousand, we thought, was the least. When we found them within gunshot, our leader ordered the two wings to advance swiftly, and give them a salvo on each wing with their shot, which was done; and wheeling off to the left, they gave over their design.

Two days after we came to the city of Naun, or Naum.

After this we passed several great rivers, and two dreadful deserts; one of which we were sixteen days passing over; and which as I said, was to be called No Man's Land, and on the 13th of April we came to the frontiers of the Muscovite dominions.

SECTION XL

ROUTE THROUGH MUSCOVY—ROBINSON AND A SCOTS MERCHANT DESTROY AN IDOL—THE WHOLE CARAVAN IN GREAT PERIL FROM THE PURSUIT OF THE PAGANS—TOBOLSKI—DEPARTURE FROM TOBOLSKI—ENCOUNTER WITH A TROOP OF ROBBERS IN THE DESERT—ROBINSON REACHES ARCHANGEL, AND FINALLY ARRIVES IN ENGLAND

As we entered into the Muscovite dominions we were very visibly obliged to the care the Czar of Muscovy has taken to have cities and towns built in as many places as it is possible to place them, where his soldiers keep garrison, something like the stationary soldiers placed by the Romans in the remotest countries of their empire. Wherever we came, though at these towns and stations the garrisons and governors were Russians and professed Christians, yet the inhabitants were mere pagans, sacrificing to idols and worshipping the sun, moon and stars, or all the host of heaven; and not only so, but were, of all the heathens and pagans that ever I met with, the most barbarous, except only that they did not eat men's flesh as our savages of America did.

Some instances of this we met within the country between Argun, where we enter the Muscovite dominions, and a city of Tartars and Russians together, called Nertzinskoi, in which is a continued desert or forest, which cost us twenty days to travel over. In a village near the last of these places, I had the curiosity to go and see their way of living, which is most brutish and insufferable; they had had, I suppose, a great sacrifice that day; for there stood out, upon an old stump of a tree, an idol made of wood, frightful as the devil; at least, as anything we can think of to represent the devil can be made: it had a head not so much as resembling any creature that the world ever saw; ears as big as goats' horns, and as high; eyes as big as a crown piece; a nose like a crooked ram's horn, and a mouth extended four-cornered, like that of a lion, with horrible teeth, hooked like a parrot's under bill: it was dressed up in the filthiest manner that you could suppose; its upper garment was of sheep-skins, with the wool outward; a great Tartar bonnet on the head, with two horns growing through it: it was about eight feet high yet had no feet or legs, nor any other proportion of parts.

This scarecrow was set up at the outer side of the village; and, when I came near to it, there were sixteen or seventeen creatures, whether men or women I could not tell, for they made no distinction by their habits, all lying flat upon the ground round this formidable block of shapeless wood. A little way off from the idol, and at the door of a tent or hut, made all of sheep-skins and cow-skins dried, stood three butchers—I thought they were such; when I came nearer to them, I found they had long knives in their hands; and in the middle of the tent appeared three sheep killed and one young bullock or steer. These, it seems, were sacrifices to that senseless log of an idol: the three men were priests belonging to it, and the seventeen prostrated wretches were the people who brought the offering, and were making their prayers to that stock.

I confess I was more moved at their stupidity and brutish worship of a hobgoblin than ever I was at anything in my life. I rode up to the image or monster, call it what you will, and with my sword made a stroke at the bonnet that was on its head, and cut it in two; and one of our men that was with me took hold of the sheep-skin that covered it, and pulled at it; when, behold, a most hideous outcry and howling ran throughout the village and two or three hundred people came about my ears, so that I was glad to scour for it, for we saw some had bows and arrows; but I resolved from that moment to visit them again.

Our caravan rested three nights at the town; so we had some leisure here to put my design in execution. I communicated my project to the Scots merchant of Moscow.

He laughed at me at first, but finding me resolute, he told me he would go with me if it cost him his life, but he would go first and bring one of his companions to go with us. He brought me a Tartar's robe or gown of sheep-skins, and a bonnet, with a bow and arrows, and had provided the same for himself and his countryman, that the people, if they saw us, should not be able to determine who we were.

All the first night we spent in mixing up some combustible matter with aqua vitæ, gunpowder, and such other materials as we could get; and, having a good quantity of tar in a little pot, about an hour after night we set out upon our expedition.

We came to the place about eleven o'clock at night, and found that the people seemed to be all at their rest; only, that in the great hut, or tent, as we called it, where we saw the three priests whom we mistook for butchers, we saw a light; and going up close to the door, we heard people talking as if there were five or six of them. We made them prisoners, tied their hands, and made them stand and see their idol destroyed by means of the combustibles we had brought with us.

We appeared in the morning among our fellow-travellers, exceeding busy in getting ready for our journey; nor could any man suggest that we had been anywhere but in our beds.

But the affair did not end so; the next day came a great number of the country people to the town gates, and in a most outrageous manner demanded satisfaction of the Russian governor for the insulting their priests and burning their Cham Chi-Thaungu. The people of Nertzinskoi were at first in a great consternation, for they said the Tartars were already no less than thirty thousand strong.

The governor was unwilling to make a breach, or to have any cause for war alleged to be given by him, the Czar having strictly charged them to treat the conquered country with gentleness and civility, gave them still all the good words he could. At last he told them there was a caravan gone towards Russia that morning, and perhaps it was some of them who had done them this injury; and that if they would be satisfied with that, he would send after them to inquire into it. This seemed to appease them a little; and accordingly the governor sent after us, and gave us a particular account how the thing was; intimating withal, that if any in our caravan had done it, they should make their escape; but that, whether we had done it or no, we should make all the haste forward that was possible; and that, in the meantime, he would keep them in play as long as he could.

The captain of the caravan for the first time took the hint that the governor gave us, and we travelled two days and two nights without any considerable stop, and then we lay at a village called Plothus; nor did we make any long stop here, but hastened on towards Jarawena. But upon the second day's march from Plothus, by the clouds of dust behind us at a great distance, some of our people began to be sensible we were pursued.

The third day, when we were encamped, the enemy came upon us in great numbers, and we only escaped them through the cunning of a Cossack of Jarawena, who telling our leader he would send these people away to Sibeilka, rode away from our rear, and, taking a great circuit about, came to the city of the Tartars, as if he had been sent express to them, and told them that the people who had burnt their Cham-Chi-Thaungu were gone to Sibeilka with a caravan of miscreants, that is to say, Christians, and that they were resolved to burn the god Scal Isarg, belonging to the Tonguses. Upon this, away the Tartars drove in a most violent hurry to Sibeilka, which, it seems was five days' journey to the north; and in less than three hours they were entirely out of our sight, and we never heard any more of them, nor whether they went to Sibeilka or no. So we passed away safely on to Jarawena, where there was a garrison of Muscovites, and there we rested five days, the caravan being exceedingly fatigued with the last day's hard march, and with want of rest in the night.

From this city we had a frightful desert, which held us twenty-three days' march. We furnished ourselves with some tents here, for the better accommodating ourselves in the night; and the leader of the caravan procured sixteen carriages, or waggons of the country, for carrying our water or provisions; and these carriages were our defence, every night, round our little camp; so that had the Tartars appeared, unless they had been very numerous indeed, they would not have been able to hurt us.

I have nothing material to say of my particular affairs till I came to Tobolski, the capital city of Siberia, where I let the caravan go, and made provision to winter.

In the month of May I began to make all ready to pack up; I had bought a considerable quantity of sables, black fox-skins, fine ermines, and such other furs as are very rich, in that city, in exchange for some of the goods I had brought from China: in particular for the cloves and nutmegs, of which I sold the greatest part here, and the rest afterwards at Archangel, for a much better price than I could have got in London; and my partner, who was sensible to the profit, and whose business more particularly than mine was merchandise, was mightily pleased with our stay, on account of the traffic we made here.

It was the beginning of June when I left this remote place, a city, I believe, little heard of in the world: and, indeed, it is so far out of the road of commerce, that I know not how it should be much talked of.

We arrived all safe at Archangel the 18th; having been a year, five months, and three days on the journey, including our stay of eight months at Tobolski. We were obliged to stay at this place six weeks for the arrival of the ships, and must have tarried longer, had not an Hamburgher come in above a month sooner than any of the English ships: when after some consideration that the city of Hamburgh might happen to be as good a market for our goods as London, we all took freight with him.

We then set sail from Archangel the 20th of August, the same year; and after no extraordinary bad voyage, arrived safe in the Elbe the 18th of September. Here my partner and I found a very good sale for our goods, as well those of China, as the sables, etc., of Siberia; and dividing the produce, my share amounted to three thousand four hundred and seventy-five pounds seventeen shillings and threepence, including about six hundred pounds' worth of diamonds which I purchased at Bengal.

To conclude, having stayed near four months in Hamburgh, I came from thence by land to The Hague, where I embarked in the packet, and arrived in London the 10th of January, 1705, having been absent from England ten years and nine months. And here I am, preparing for a longer journey than all these, having lived a life of infinite variety seventy-two years, and learned sufficiently to know the value of retirement, and the blessing of ending our days in peace.

THE END